Common Core

Standards for Mathematical Content

Domain Counting and Cardinality

Cluster Compare numbers.

Cluster Know number names and the count sequence.

Standards K.CC.2, K.CC.4.c, K.CC.6, K.CC.7, K.OA.1

Standards for Mathematical Practice

- ✔ Make sense of problems and persevere in solving them.
- ✔ Reason abstractly and quantitatively.
- ✔ Construct viable arguments and critique the reasoning of others.
- ✔ Model with mathematics.
- ✔ Use appropriate tools strategically.
- ✔ Attend to precision.
- ✔ Look for and make use of structure.
- ✔ Look for and express regularity in repeated reasoning.

Comparing and Ordering Numbers 0 to 10

Planning

Math Background 65A
Differentiated Instruction 65C
The Language of Math 65D
Topic Centers 65E
Interactive Math Story 65G
Topic Opener 65
Math Project 🎨 Art 66

Lessons

4-1 Comparing Numbers Through 10 .... 67A
4-2 Comparing Numbers to 5 .... 69A
4-3 Comparing Numbers to 10 .... 71A
4-4 1 More 73A
4-5 1 Fewer 75A
4-6 2 More 77A
4-7 2 Fewer 79A
4-8 Ordering Numbers Through 10 .... 81A
4-9 Ordering Numbers on a Number Line 83A
4-10 Problem Solving Use Objects 85A

Review and Assessment

Reteaching and Technology 87
Topic 4 Test 89
Performance Assessment 90
Benchmark Test Topics 1–4 .... 90A

Copyright © 2012 by Pearson Education, Inc., or its affiliates. All Rights Reserved. Printed in the United States of America. This publication is protected by copyright, and permission should be obtained from the publisher prior to any prohibited reproduction, storage in a retrieval system, or transmission in any form or by any means, electronic, mechanical, photocopying, recording, or likewise. For information regarding permissions, write to Rights Management & Contracts, Pearson Education, Inc., One Lake Street, Upper Saddle River, New Jersey 07458.

Pearson, Scott Foresman, Pearson Scott Foresman, and enVisionMATH are trademarks, in the U.S. and/or in other countries, of Pearson Education Inc., or its affiliates.

Common Core State Standards: © Copyright 2010. National Governors Association Center for Best Practices and Council of Chief State School Officers. All rights reserved.

"Understanding by Design" is registered as a trademark with the United States Patent and Trademark Office by the Association for Supervision of Curriculum Development (ASCD). ASCD claims exclusive trademark rights in the terms "Understanding by Design" and the abbreviation "UbD".

Pearson Education has incorporated the concepts of the Understanding by Design methodology into this text in consultation with [contributing author/editor] Grant Wiggins, [one of the] creator[s] of the Understanding by Design methodology. The Association for Supervision of Curriculum Development (ASCD), publisher of the "Understanding by Design Handbook" co-authored by Grant Wiggins, has not authorized, approved or sponsored this work and is in no way affiliated with Pearson or its products.

ISBN-13: 978-0-328-67326-1
ISBN-10: 0-328-67326-9

4 5 6 7 8 9 10 V003 15 14 13 12 11

MATH BACKGROUND

BIG IDEA **Comparison and Relationships** Numbers, expressions, measures, and objects can be compared and related to other numbers, expressions, measures, and objects in different ways.

ESSENTIAL UNDERSTANDINGS

4-1   In a pair of numbers, the number that shows more is greater. The number that shows fewer is less.

4-2   You can use 5 as a benchmark to compare numbers.

4-3   You can use 10 as a benchmark to compare numbers.

4-4   *1 more than* expresses a relationship between two numbers.

4-5   *1 fewer than* expresses a relationship between two numbers.

4-6   *2 more than* expresses a relationship between two numbers.

4-7   *2 fewer than* expresses a relationship between two numbers.

4-8   There is a specific order to the set of whole numbers.

BIG IDEA **Numbers and the Number Line** The set of real numbers is infinite and ordered. Whole numbers, integers, and fractions are real numbers. Each real number can be associated with a unique point on the number line.

ESSENTIAL UNDERSTANDING

4-9   Numbers can be shown by a unique point on the number line. The distance between any two consecutive whole numbers on a given number line is always the same.

BIG IDEA **Practices, Processes, and Proficiencies** Mathematics content and practices can be applied to solve problems.

ESSENTIAL UNDERSTANDING

4-10   Some problems can be solved by using objects to act out the actions in a problem.

Comparing Numbers

More and Fewer

Before developing an understanding of or language for specific numbers, young children can identify and create equivalent sets by matching each object in one set with exactly one object from a second set. Based on this understanding of equal quantities, young children can compare sets to determine whether a set has more or fewer elements than another and can create a set that has one more or one fewer than a given set. Children can draw on these experiences with relative size to order numbers as they begin to learn number names and symbols.

Number Relationships

Children can apply their skills of counting, comparing sets, and recognizing one more to order the numbers through ten. As they connect their knowledge of the counting sequence and the relative values of the quantities, they can answer questions such as "Which number comes before seven?" and "Which number comes after nine?"

Because ten is such an important benchmark in our number system, children should be able to visualize the relationships between ten and numbers less than ten. A ten-frame is a powerful tool for exploring these relationships. For example, when eight counters are displayed in a ten-frame, it is easy to see that eight, represented by five and three more, is two less than ten.

Mathematical Practices: Model with Mathematics

Review *more* and *fewer* by modeling sets that have obvious differences in quantities, such as 5 blocks and 20 blocks.

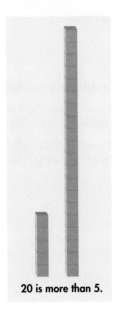

20 is more than 5.

Mathematical Practices: Use Structure

To reinforce correct number order, display groups of 1 to 10 objects in order and have children match number cards to the correct groups.

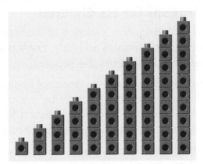

For a complete list of *enVisionMATH* Professional Development resources in print, on DVD, and online, see the *Teacher's Program Overview*.

 INTERVENTION

ELL

Considerations for ELL Children

Repeated oral language practice of the terms that are used to compare numbers will help English learners remember and understand the process.

- **Beginning** Compare two unequal groups of objects, using the word *greater* to describe the group that has more. Then compare the two groups again, using the word *less* to describe the group that has fewer.

- **Intermediate** Model the above activity and then have children repeat it, using the words *greater* and *less*.

- **Advanced** Have children create two groups of objects that have an unequal number of objects. Have children compare the groups, using the words *greater* and *less*.

Special Needs

Considerations for Special Needs Children

- Demonstrate with special needs children the order of numbers 1 through 10 by using their fingers to count. Have children start counting with their pinkies, instead of their thumbs, so they do not have trouble keeping their ring and pinky fingers down.

- Understanding number order will help children compare numbers.

- Help children see that when we count, the next number is always *1 more* than the given number, and the number before is always *1 less*.

Below Level

Considerations for Below Level Children

- Some children may need extra practice to master comparing numbers.

- For children who have trouble identifying *more* and *fewer* numbers of items, have them use one-to-one correspondence to match items.

Advanced/Gifted

Considerations for Advanced/Gifted Children

- Some children will be able to extend their knowledge and number sense.

- Provide advanced children with ample opportunities to practice mental math in which they compare numbers.

Response to Intervention

 RTI **Ongoing Intervention**
- Lessons with guiding questions to assess understanding
- Support to prevent misconceptions and to reteach

 RTI **Strategic Intervention**
- Targeted to small groups who need more support
- Easy to implement

 RTI **Intensive Intervention**
- Instruction to accelerate progress
- Instruction focused on foundational skills

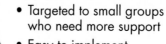

MATHEMATICAL PRACTICES

Reading Comprehension and Problem Solving

Use Structure:

Using Reading Comprehension Strategies

A good reading comprehension strategy to use in math is draw and discuss visual images based on text descriptions. (Draw a picture.)

Questions to Guide Comprehension

Use these comprehension questions with Exercise 1 in Lesson 4-10.

What do you need to find out? [How many frogs are there?] *What do you know?* [You can use counters to help find how many.]

Act It Out!

How can you use counters to show how many? Give children counters and have them place 1 counter on each picture of a frog. Then they place 1 more counter to find how many.

Talk It Out!

Encourage children to make up a story as they model each problem with counters. Have them explain how they solved each problem.

Draw It Out!

How could you draw a picture of how you solved each problem? Have children draw a counter for each animal in the picture and then draw 1 more. They write the total number below their picture.

Lesson 4-10, Exercise 1

Vocabulary Activities

Greater or Less

Attend to Precision Use number cards for 1–10 (or Teaching Tool 5) and two-color counters (or Teaching Tool 32). Have children choose a number card and make a matching group of counters. Partners compare the counters and numbers to tell who has more or fewer counters and which number is greater or less. Children should use the words *greater than* and *less than* as they compare their counters.

Math Center

Which Is More?

Materials
Pair of dot cubes

- Have partners take turns rolling the cubes. One partner states the two numbers represented by the cubes. The other partner tells which cube represents more.
- Partners then switch roles.

Art Center

Show More, Show Fewer

Materials
Easel paper, paint

- Partner A and Partner B both decide on what to draw such as beachballs, suns, or cats. Or you may wish to assign objects to each pair.
- Partner A paints 5 objects.
- Partner B paints 1 or 2 more or 1 or 2 fewer.
- When the pair has finished, they show and discuss their paintings.

Reading/Language Center

Count 'Em Up!

Materials
Two classic children's books such as *The Story of Babar* or *Make Way for Ducklings*

- Partners "read" together, looking at the pictures and counting various objects in the pictures.
- Then they go through one book together, page by page and compare the pages: "There are more ducks on this page than there were on the other page. There are two fewer trees on this page. There are zero animals here, but two on the next page."

Some trees grow in a forest.

Some trees grow on an island

Line 'Em Up!

Materials
5–10 stones or shells of different sizes, 5–10 different sized blocks, Number Cards 0–10 (Teaching Tool 5)

- Partners work together to arrange the stones by size and place a number card in front of each one to indicate the size order.
- Once the order is set, children can play a game by mixing up the stones and their numbers and inviting another child to put them in order again.

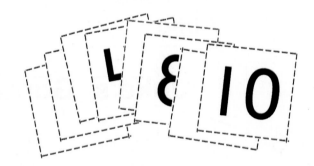

Spending Money

Materials
Pennies

- "Mother" has 5 children who want to go shopping. She gives each child a group of pennies, anywhere from 1 to 10 pennies.
- "Father" lines up the "children" according to the number of pennies they have. "Amy has 6 pennies. Who has 1 more than 6?" That person stands next to Amy. "Who has 2 fewer than Amy?"
- Once the children are lined up correctly, Father takes them shopping.

Sandy Numbers

Materials
Cookie cutters, sand tools

- Wet the sand in the sand/water table.
- Have partners work together to press groups of up to 10 shapes in the sand using cookie cutters.
- Have them take turns choosing a number from 1–10. Children can show that many shapes, and then write the number in the sand.
- They compare their groups and decide which group has more and which group has fewer.

Jake's Garden

This is a story in which children count rows in a garden from 5 to 10 and compare which pages depict more or fewer than the ones before and after.

1 ▶ Before the Story

Picture Walk

Hold up the book and read the title, author's name, and illustrator's name to children. Look at the pages. *Who are the characters in this story?* [A boy named Jake and two other people, who may be his grandparents]

What time of year does this story take place? Why do you think so? Have children check the first page again and compare it to the last page. *Has time gone by? How do you know?* [Yes. On the first page, there aren't any plants growing in the garden. On the last page, the garden is full of plants and the people are wearing warmer clothes.]

Activate Prior Knowledge

Jake and his grandparents plant row after row of seeds. In this story we will count as they add more and more rows. Hold up four crayons. *How many crayons do I have?* [4] Pick up one more crayon. *How many more crayons do I have now?* [1 more] Pick up two more crayons. *Do I have more or fewer crayons?* [More] *How many more?* [2 more]

This book belongs to:

Alma

Topic 4 Story

Jake's Garden

Written by Paige Levinsky
Illustrated by Sheree Boyd

Plant with me.
Let's make rows.
1, 2, 3, 4, __5__ rows.

Topic 4 ❶

Plant with me.
Let's make 1 more
Now we have __6__
rows.

Topic 4 ❷

2 ▶ During the Story

READ

Read the story aloud for enjoyment. Then read each page aloud and wait for children to respond to the text. Make sure children understand that the seed packets indicate the rows planted.

GESTURE

Have children point to and count aloud the number of rows on the first page of the story. [1, 2, 3, 4, 5] Have them point and count to the rows on the second page. *How many more rows are there?* [1] *Which page, 1 or 2, shows the fewer number of rows?* [Page 1] Have them turn to the third page and count again. *How many more rows are there on this page?* [2 more] Continue counting rows.

lant with me.
et's make more rows.
low we have ___8___
ows.

Topic 4 ● 3

You planted with me.
Now we have __10__
rows.
A garden for me!

fold down

Topic 4 ● 4

Extension

Have children share an activity they enjoy doing with their grandparents or older family members. Encourage them to either draw pictures about the activity or possibly act out an activity for others to guess.

You may wish to have children take home their Interactive Math Story books and share what they have learned about 1 more and 2 more.

COLOR

Distribute the Interactive Math Story books to children. Direct children's attention to page 1. Have them circle 5 flowers yellow. On page 2, have them circle 6 flowers red. On page 3, have them add 1 more flower to the picture, and on page 4, have them add 2 more birds to the sky.

WRITE

Revisit the first page of the story. Count aloud with children the five rows in the garden, and have them write 5 on the line. Read aloud the text on page 2 and have children count the rows, and then write 6. Continue doing the same for the next two pages. [Children write 8 and then 10.]

SPEAK

Invite children to retell the story in their own words. Encourage children to talk about the vegetables that are planted.

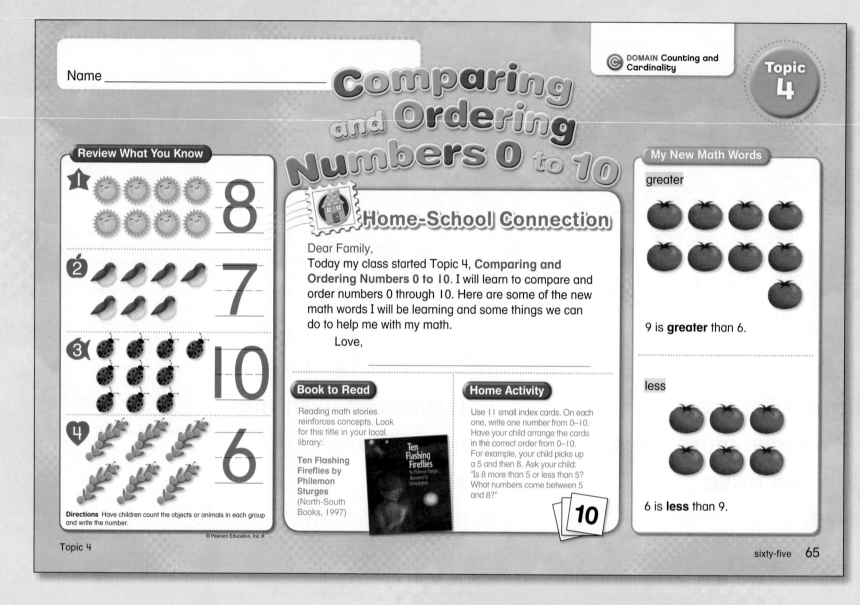

Name _____

DOMAIN **Counting and Cardinality**

Topic **4**

Comparing and Ordering Numbers 0 to 10

Review What You Know

1. 🌻🌻🌻🌻 🌻🌻🌻🌻 **8**

2. 🐦🐦🐦🐦 🐦🐦🐦 **7**

3. 🐞🐞🐞🐞 🐞🐞🐞🐞 🐞🐞 **10**

4. 🌿🌿🌿🌿🌿🌿 🌿🌿🌿🌿🌿🌿 **6**

Directions Have children count the objects or animals in each group and write the number.

© Pearson Education, Inc. K

Home-School Connection

Dear Family,

Today my class started Topic 4, **Comparing and Ordering Numbers 0 to 10.** I will learn to compare and order numbers 0 through 10. Here are some of the new math words I will be learning and some things we can do to help me with my math.

Love,

_____

Book to Read

Reading math stories reinforces concepts. Look for this title in your local library:

Ten Flashing Fireflies by Philemon Sturges (North-South Books, 1997)

Home Activity

Use 11 small index cards. On each one, write one number from 0–10. Have your child arrange the cards in the correct order from 0–10. For example, your child picks up a 5 and then 8. Ask your child: "Is 8 more than 5 or less than 5? What numbers come between 5 and 8?"

10

My New Math Words

greater

🍅🍅🍅🍅 🍅🍅🍅🍅 🍅

9 is **greater** than 6.

less

🍅🍅🍅 🍅🍅🍅

6 is **less** than 9.

Review What You Know

Purpose

Diagnose children's readiness by assessing prerequisite content. Assign each set of exercises and go over the answers with children.

Understanding by Design

Children will be able to answer the Topic Essential Question by the end of the topic. Revisit the question throught the topic. Then use the Topic 4 Performance Assessment.

Topic Essential Question

• How can numbers from 0 to 10 be compared and ordered?

Cards can always be used as flash cards. Have children create large vocabulary cards with visuals to add to the classroom word wall.

less

More and Fewer In the Garden

What You Need

10 counters
●●●●●●●●●●
paper clip
pencil
10 paper squares

How to Play

1. Spin the spinner. Say the number.
2. Show that number of counters in the top row.
3. Your partner spins and shows counters in the bottom row.
4. Take a paper square if your group has more.
5. The first player to get 5 squares is the winner.

Topic 4

sixty-six 66

Game
for school or home

Purpose

Provide children with an opportunity to practice prerequisite skills. Before they begin the game, you may wish to discuss with children how to figure out if one number is greater than another. Explain that children can count quietly to themselves from 0 to determine which number is greater.

Math Project

Art

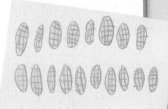

Directions

Anytime after completing Lesson 4-3, have children draw pictures comparing numbers to 10. For example, have children draw 2 rows of vegetables that grow in your state. The top row should have more or fewer than 10; the bottom row should have 10. Children may want to make several drawings over multiple days. When they have completed their drawings, bring the class together to discuss them. Have children describe their pictures, comparing the two rows of vegetables.

Publish children's pictures in a class book.

66

Domain
Counting and Cardinality

Cluster
Compare numbers.

Standards
K.CC.6 Identify whether the number of objects in one group is greater than, less than, or equal to the number of objects in another group, e.g., by using matching and counting strategies. Also **K.CC.7**

Mathematical Practices

☑ Make sense of problems and persevere in solving them.

☑ Reason abstractly and quantitatively.

○ Construct viable arguments and critique the reasoning of others.

○ Model with mathematics.

☑ Use appropriate tools strategically.

☑ Attend to precision.

☑ Look for and make use of structure.

○ Look for and express regularity in repeated reasoning.

Comparing Numbers Through 10

 **and Easy** Lesson Overview

Objective	Essential Understanding	Vocabulary	Materials
Children will compare two numbers using sets of objects and one-to-one correspondence to determine which number is greater and which is less.	In a pair of numbers, the number that shows more is greater. The number that shows fewer is less.	**greater** **less**	Counters (Teaching Tool 32), crayons

PROFESSIONAL DEVELOPMENT

Math Background

Children have previously learned how to use one-to-one correspondence to compare sets. They have also compared numbers. In this lesson, children use the number ten as a benchmark. Ten is important because of our base-ten numeration system.

1 Daily Common Core Review

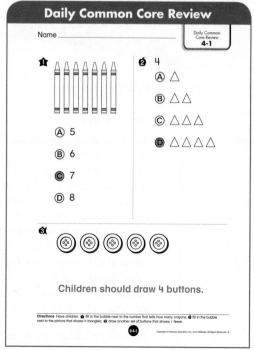

Children should draw 4 buttons.

Also available in print

Content Reviewed

Exercise 1   Use Numbers to Describe How Many

Exercise 2   Count Objects

Exercise 3   One Fewer

 30 min ## Problem-Based Interactive Learning

Overview Children will make sets, count items in the sets, and compare numbers.

Focus How do you know which number is greater than another?

Materials Counters (Teaching Tool 32), crayons

Vocabulary greater, less

 **Engage**

Set the Purpose Remind children that they have learned that numbers tell how many. *You will learn how to compare numbers in this lesson.*

Connect Have children hold up 3 fingers on one hand and 5 fingers on the other hand. *Which hand shows more fingers? Hold it high in the air. Which hand shows fewer fingers? Hold it low.*

 **MATHEMATICAL PRACTICES**

Reason Quantitatively
Remind children that they know how to count items in a set and use numbers to tell how many.

Pose the Problem *Grandma is planting seedlings, or little plants. She plants 5 red pepper seedlings and 7 yellow pepper seedlings. How can we find out which number is greater?*

Academic Vocabulary Write the numbers 5 and 7 on the board. Point out that 7 is **greater** than 5. Point out that 5 is **less** than 7.

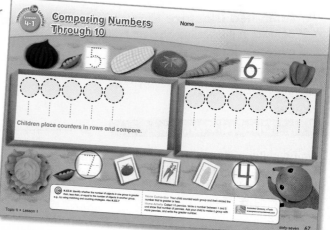

Model Make a row of 5 red counters for 5 seedlings on the workmat. Have children do the same. Trace the number 5. *Then Grandma plants 7 yellow pepper seedlings.* Make a row of 7 yellow counters below the 5 counters as you count aloud. Place each yellow counter at the end of a line so 5 are matched one-to-one. Place 2 extra counters in the row. Have children do the same. Now trace each line from top to bottom. *Does every line have a counter?* [Yes] *Are there more yellow counters than lines?* [Yes] *Let's count the yellow counters. How many counters are there in this group?* [7] *Trace the number 7. The row with 7 counters has extra counters that don't match up. That means that the number 7 is greater than 5, or 5 is less than 7.*

Small-Group Interaction *Now Grandma is going to plant 6 red pepper plants and 4 yellow pepper plants.* Have children write the numbers 6 and 4. *Which row has fewer counters? How do you know?* [4 is less than 6, or 6 is greater than 4. The row with 6 counters has extra counters that don't match up.] Have children circle the number on the left mat that is greater (7) and the number on the right that is less (4).

 Extend

When you count, does 10 come before or after 8? How can you tell by counting that 10 is greater than 8? [Since 10 comes after 8, I know that 10 is the greater number.]

 eTools **Counters** www.pearsonsuccessnet.com

Visual Learning

How many tomatoes are there? Let's count. Point and say the number. [3]

Let's count the row of peppers. Point and say the number. [7] *Are there more tomatoes or peppers?* [More peppers] *How do you know?* [When I match the tomatoes and peppers, there are some extra peppers.] *Which number is greater, 3 or 7?* [7] *Which number is less?* [3]

1 Visual Learning

Set the Purpose Call children's attention to the **Visual Learning Bridge** at the top of the page. *In this lesson, you will learn about comparing numbers through 10.*

 Animated Glossary Children can see highlighted words defined in the Online Student Edition.

greater, **less**

www.pearsonsuccessnet.com

2 Guided Practice

Remind children that the group that has more items matches the number that is greater. The group with fewer items matches the number that is less.

Exercise 2
Error Intervention

If children do not understand why they are tracing lines to match one to one,

then use counters and craft sticks to help children visualize the comparisons.

Do you understand? *Is 8 greater than 9 or less than 9? How do you know?* [It is less than 9 because if you match up rows of counters, the row with 9 has an extra counter.]

Reteaching Line up children in two unequal groups. Have the groups face each other and hold hands to form as many one-to-one matches as possible. Count children in each group and talk about which group has more or fewer and which number is greater or less.

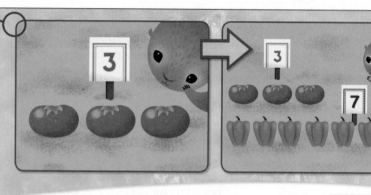

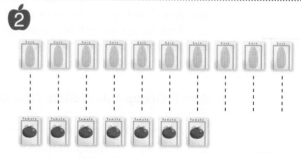

Directions Have children trace a line from each item in the top row to each item in the bottom row. Then have them count and trace or write each number. Then have them circle the greater number.

Topic 4 • Lesson 1

ELL
STRATEGY
Visual
Learning

Visual Learning Animation

www.pearsonsuccessnet.com or CD

How many carrots are in this row? Count aloud as you point to each one. [10]

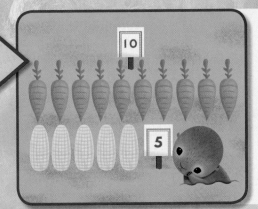

Are there more carrots or corn? Let's count the row of corn. How many corn are there? [5] Which number is greater, 10 or 5? [10] Which row has fewer? [The row of corn] Which number is less, 10 or 5? [5]

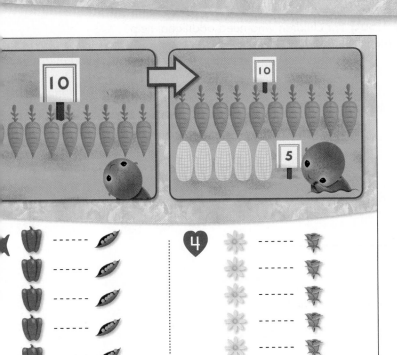

Directions Have children draw a line from each item in one group to each item in the other group. Then have them count and write the number. Then have them circle the number that is less.

sixty-eight 68

---

3 Independent Practice

Children draw lines from each item in one group to each item in the other group. They count and write the number of items. Children circle the lesser number.

Count and Compare

🕐 10 min 👥

Materials (per pair) Number Cards 1–10 (Teaching Tool 5), 10 blue and 10 green color tiles (Teaching Tool 32)

- Have pairs shuffle number cards for 1 through 10 and place them facedown. Each child draws a card and places that many color tiles in a column.

- Partners compare their columns to see who has more or fewer. They then compare the numbers on their cards to see which number is greater and which number is less.

- Repeat, having children draw additional cards.

68A

Close

Essential Understanding In a pair of numbers, the number that shows more is greater. The number that shows fewer is less. *Remember, when comparing two numbers, the number that shows more is greater.*

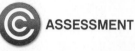 **ASSESSMENT**

Exercise 1 is worth 1 point.
Use the rubric to score Exercise 2.

Exercise 2

Use Appropriate Tools Children should be able to draw more than 4 suns and write the greater number.

ELL Model Thinking Aloud For children who need additional help in counting, have them touch each sun as they count aloud.

Student Samples
3-point answer Children draw 5–10 suns, write the number, and show one-to-one correspondence.

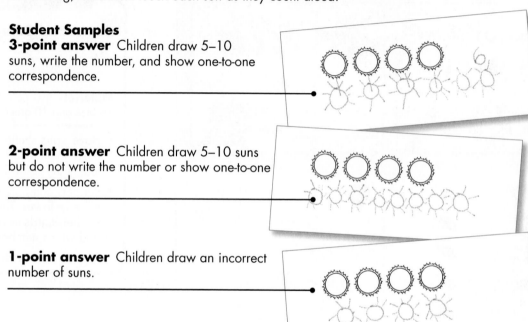

2-point answer Children draw 5–10 suns but do not write the number or show one-to-one correspondence.

1-point answer Children draw an incorrect number of suns.

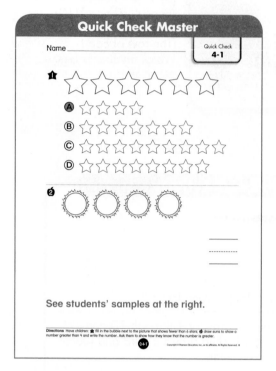

Quick Check Master

Name _____

Quick Check
4-1

See students' samples at the right.

 Formative Assessment

Use the **Quick Check** to assess children's understanding.

Prescription for Differentiated Instruction
Use children's work on the **Quick Check** to prescribe differentiated instruction.

Points	Prescription
0–2	Intervention
3	On-Level
4	Advanced

Differentiated Instruction

Intervention

Comparing Cube Trains

  10 min

Materials (per group) 30 blue connecting cubes

- Make a 5-cube train and count the cubes aloud. *Now I will make a train with 1 more cube. There are 6 cubes in this train.*

- Repeat with 1 fewer cube for a 4-cube train. Compare the 3 trains and guide children to say with you, *6 is greater than 5. 4 is less than 5.*

- Repeat with numbers 1 through 10.

ELL Partner Talk Listen for the word *zero*. A player might say, "My number is zero, so I do not have to put any squares on the workmat."

Leveled Homework

Reteaching Master

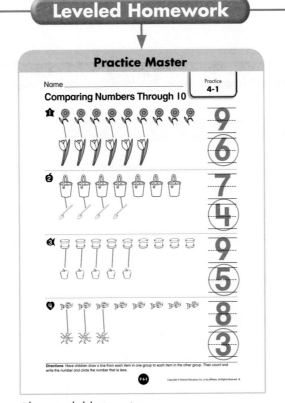

Also available in print

Practice Master

Also available in print

Enrichment Master

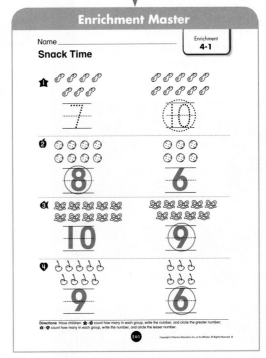

Also available in print

 eTools **Counters**
www.pearsonsuccessnet.com

DIGITAL eTools **Counters**
www.pearsonsuccessnet.com

DIGITAL eTools **Counters**
www.pearsonsuccessnet.com

68C

Domain
Counting and Cardinality

Cluster
Compare numbers.

Standards
K.CC.6 Identify whether the number of objects in one group is greater than, less than, or equal to the number of objects in another group, e.g., by using matching and counting strategies. Also **K.CC.7**

Mathematical Practices

✔ Make sense of problems and persevere in solving them.

✔ Reason abstractly and quantitatively.

✔ Construct viable arguments and critique the reasoning of others.

○ Model with mathematics.

✔ Use appropriate tools strategically.

○ Attend to precision.

✔ Look for and make use of structure.

✔ Look for and express regularity in repeated reasoning.

Comparing Numbers to 5

 **Lesson Overview**

Objective	Essential Understanding	Vocabulary	Materials
Given a number from 0–5, children will tell if the number is greater or less than 5.	You can use 5 as a benchmark to compare numbers.		Number Cards 1–11 (Teaching Tool 5), Counters (Teaching Tool 32)

 PROFESSIONAL DEVELOPMENT

Math Background

Research says ... Children who are mentally and actively engaged in adjusting and constructing sets to compare quantities exhibit developing understanding of number relationships (Kamii, 1985).

In this lesson, children will relate a given number to 5. The most important tool for this relationship is the five-frame.

1 Daily Common Core Review

Daily Common Core Review

Name _____

Daily Common Core Review **4-2**

❶
Ⓐ Ⓒ
Ⓑ Ⓓ

❷
Ⓐ Ⓒ
Ⓑ Ⓓ

❸
☆ ☆ ☆ ☆ ☆

6 6

Directions Have children: ★ fill in the bubble next to the picture that shows the fish bowl with 0 fish; ❶ fill in the bubble next to the picture that shows 2 birds on the branch; ❷ count the stars and write the number two times on the lines.

0-2

Content Reviewed
Exercise 1   Count Objects
Exercise 2   Count Objects
Exercise 3   Use Numbers to Describe How Many

Also available in print

 ◑ 30 min # Problem-Based Interactive Learning

Overview Children will model numbers and compare to find numbers that are greater than 5 and less than 5.

Focus How can you use 5 as a benchmark to compare numbers?

Materials Counters (Teaching Tool 32), Number Cards 1–11 (Teaching Tool 5)

Engage

Set the Purpose Remind children that they have learned how to compare numbers. *You will learn how to compare numbers to the number 5 in this lesson.*

Connect Display number cards 1–10. Ask a volunteer to choose a number card, hold it up, and say the number aloud. Have another volunteer choose another number and do the same. Ask: *Which number is less? Which number is greater?*

 MATHEMATICAL PRACTICES

Model with Mathematics
Ask children how to find numbers that are greater than 5 and less than 5.

Pose the Problem *Grandpa bought 6 strawberries. Is 6 greater or less than 5? How can we find out?* Have children share their ideas before modeling the comparison.

Model Move 5 counters onto the workmat and have children do the same. Count with children. Place one more counter next to the five-frame and have children do the same. Count again. *I know that 6 counters are more than 5 counters. I know that the number 6 is greater than the number 5 or 5 is less than 6. How many counters are on the frame?* [5] Have children remove the counters. *Let's color in the counters to show 5. Now we need to show 1 more counter. Let's draw 1 counter below the mat. How many counters do we have now?* [6] *Which number should we trace to show how many counters we colored in?* [6] Have children trace 6. *Now let's circle 6 because it is greater than 5.*

Use Math Manipulatives Make sure that children understand that the five-frame always shows 5 when there is a counter in each square.

Small-Group Interaction Have children complete the page while you tell this story: *Grandma has 3 oranges. Is 3 greater or less than 5?* [less than]

Extend *What are some numbers that are less than 5?* [0, 1, 2, 3, 4]

 DIGITAL eTools **Counters** www.pearsonsuccessnet.com

Visual Learning

How many pineapples are there? [5] How do you know? [There is a pineapple in each square of the five-frame.]

1 Visual Learning

Set the Purpose Call children's attention to the **Visual Learning Bridge** at the top of the page. *In this lesson, you will compare numbers and decide if a number is greater than 5 or less than 5.*

2 Guided Practice

Remind children that they can compare numbers to 5.

Exercise 2
Error Intervention

If children have difficulty determining whether a number is greater or less than 5,

then have them make a row of 5 counters and a row of the other number. Guide them to use one-to-one correspondence.

Do you understand? *How can you tell if a number is greater than 5 by using a five-frame?* [You can use counters to show the number. If there are extra counters, the number is greater than 5.]

Reteaching Ask children to count small groups of objects around the room, such as crayons. Have children represent what they have counted by placing counters on and below a five-frame (Teaching Tool 10). If they display more than 5 counters, have them circle the counters with a yarn loop. Ask children to compare the counters to 5 using *greater than*, for example, "7 is greater than 5." Repeat the process for *fewer than* 5 counters and numbers less than 5.

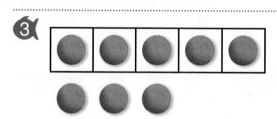

Directions Have children count how many in each row and trace or write each number. Then have them circle the if it is greater than 5.

Topic 4 • Lesson 2

How many pineapples are there now? [6] Point to each pineapple as you count aloud with children. *Is 6 greater than 5 or less than 5?* [Greater than 5] *How do you know?* [The five-frame is full and there is one extra.]

How many pineapples are there now? [2] Point to each pineapple as you count aloud with children. *Is 2 greater than 5 or less than 5?* [Less than 5] *How do you know?* [There are empty squares in the five-frame.]

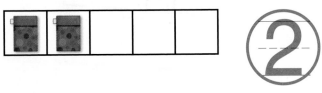

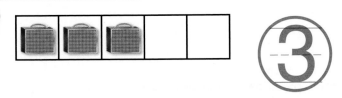

ions Have children count how many in each row, and write the number. Then have them circle the number if it is
an 5.

seventy **70**

Sorting by Sight

⏱ 10 min 👥

Materials (per pair) Number Dot Cards 1–10 (Teaching Tool 10), masking tape

- Tape the 5-dot card to a table. Make 2 tape rectangles to the right and left of the card. Place the other cards facedown.

- Partners take turns drawing cards. Tell them to study the card without counting the dots.

- If the card drawn shows a number less than 5, they put it in the left rectangle. If the number is more than 5, they put the card in the right rectangle.

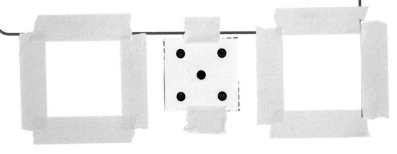

3 **Independent Practice**

Children count how many there are in each row and write the number. They circle the number if it is less than 5.

Close

Essential Understanding You can use 5 as a benchmark to compare numbers. *Remember to count the number of objects to see if there are fewer than or more than 5.*

 ASSESSMENT

Exercise 1 is worth 1 point.
Use the rubric to score Exercise 2.

Exercise 2

Attend to Precision Children should be able to draw 0–4 counters and write the number.

ELL Model Thinking Aloud For children who need additional help, have them point to and count the five boxes in the five-frame. Then have them put counters in some of the boxes and point to and count the counters.

Student Samples
3-point answer Children draw up to 4 counters and write the number.

2-point answer Children draw up to 4 counters but write an incorrect number.

1-point answer Children draw more than 4 counters.

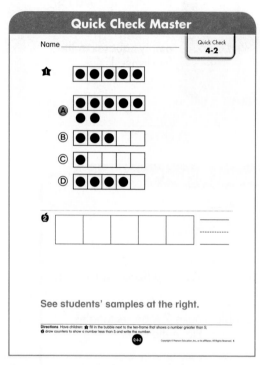

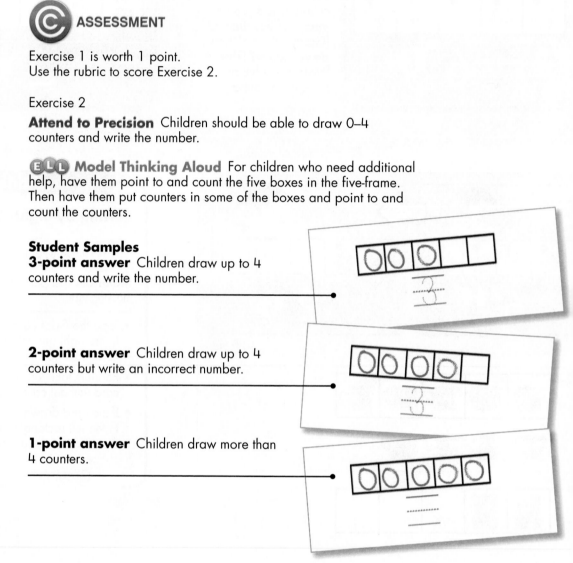

Quick Check Master

Name _____

Quick Check 4-2

See students' samples at the right.

Formative Assessment

Use the **Quick Check** to assess children's understanding.

Prescription for Differentiated Instruction
Use children's work on the **Quick Check** to prescribe differentiated instruction.

Points	Prescription
0–2	Intervention
3	On-Level
4	Advanced

Differentiated Instruction

Intervention

More Than 5, Less Than 5

🕐 10 min 👥

Materials (per pair) 2 copies of Number Dot Cards 1–10 (Teaching Tool 10)

- Put a 5 card on a table and remove the other 5 card. Place the remaining cards facedown.

- Each child picks a card. If the number is more than 5, the child says "more" and takes both cards. If both partners' cards show more than 5, cards are returned to the pile.

- Play continues until one child holds all the cards. Repeat the game in a similar manner for numbers less than 5 having the child say "less" when a number is less than 5.

On-Level

Practice / **Center Activity**

Advanced

Practice / **Center Activity**

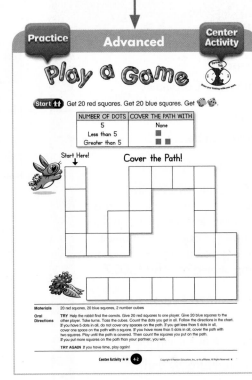

ELL Partner Talk Listen for evidence that a child is saying the words *greater than* and *less than*.

Leveled Homework

Reteaching Master

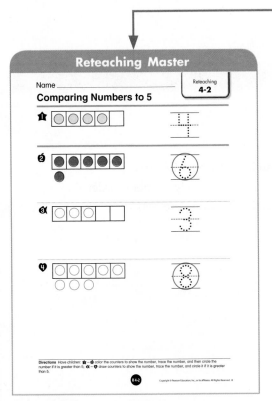

Also available in print

eTools **Counters**
www.pearsonsuccessnet.com

Practice Master

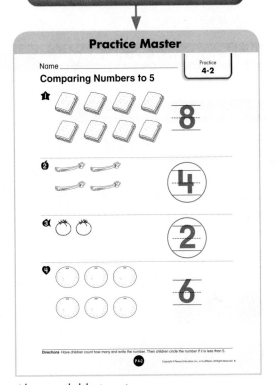

Also available in print

eTools **Counters**
www.pearsonsuccessnet.com

Enrichment Master

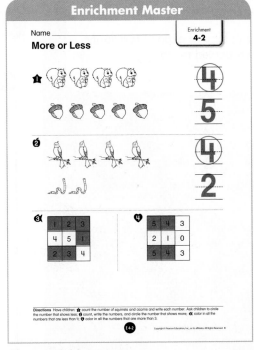

Also available in print

eTools **Counters**
www.pearsonsuccessnet.com

Comparing Numbers to 10

 **Lesson Overview**

Domain

Counting and Cardinality

Cluster

Compare numbers.

Standards

K.CC.6 Identify whether the number of objects in one group is greater than, less than, or equal to the number of objects in another group, e.g., by using matching and counting strategies. Also **K.CC.7**

Mathematical Practices

✔ Make sense of problems and persevere in solving them.

✔ Reason abstractly and quantitatively.

○ Construct viable arguments and critique the reasoning of others.

○ Model with mathematics.

✔ Use appropriate tools strategically.

○ Attend to precision.

✔ Look for and make use of structure.

✔ Look for and express regularity in repeated reasoning.

Objective	Essential Understanding	Vocabulary	Materials
Given a number or set from 0–12, children will decide if the number is greater or less than 10.	You can use 10 as a benchmark to compare numbers.		Counters (or Teaching Tool 32)

© **PROFESSIONAL DEVELOPMENT**

Math Background

Once again we want to help children relate a given number to 10. The most important tool for this relationship is the ten-frame. Children should always fill in the top row first, starting on the left. When the top row is full, counters are placed on the bottom row, starting on the left.

1 Daily Common Core Review

Daily Common Core Review

Name _____

Daily Common Core Review **4-3**

❶
Ⓐ 2
Ⓑ 3
Ⓒ 4
Ⓓ 5

❷
Ⓐ 0 1 2 3 4 5
Ⓑ 5 4 0 1 3 2
Ⓒ 0 3 4 5 2 1
Ⓓ 5 4 0 1 2 3

❸

Directions Have children: ❶ fill in the bubble next to the number that tells how many beach balls; ❷ fill in the bubble next to the group of numbers that are in the correct order; ❸ circle the row that shows more shapes.

D4-3

Content Reviewed

Exercise 1   Count Objects

Exercise 2   Identify Number Order

Exercise 3   Compare Sets

Also available in print

 30 min

Problem-Based Interactive Learning

Overview Children will model and compare to find numbers that are greater than 10 and less than 10.

Focus How can you tell if a number is less than 10?

Materials Counters (Teaching Tool 32)

Set the Purpose Remind children that they have learned how to compare numbers to the number 5. *You will learn how to compare numbers to the number 10 in this lesson.*

Connect Hold up 10 fingers. *How many fingers do I have? Do I have more ears or more fingers? Do I have more fingers or more teeth?*

MATHEMATICAL PRACTICES

Model with Mathematics
Remind children they have learned how to tell if a number was less than 10 or more than 10.

Pose the Problem Display a group of 12 counters. *Mr. Brown has horses on his farm. I have a counter to show each horse. Does he have more than 10 horses or less than 10 horses? How can we find out?* Have children share their ideas.

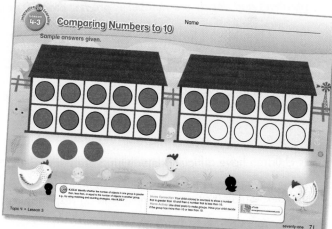

Model Display your 12 counters and move 10 counters to the workmat and have children do the same. *I know there are 10 counters here, because there are 10 squares on this frame.* Then place 2 more counters under the ten-frame and have children do the same on the workmat. *I have extra counters. Now I know that Mr. Brown has more than 10 horses.* Model as you tell a story about 14 dogs on the farm. Guide children to see that 14 counters are more than 10. Continue as above without naming the greater number. *Now show a number greater than 10 by first coloring in the 10 circles on your mat and then drawing 1 or more extra counters. How do you know you showed more than 10 counters?* Children should realize that coloring in all the outlines on the frame shows 10 and anything extra means more than 10.

Small-Group Interaction Have partners complete the page by listening to this story: *Mrs. Brown has 9 chickens on her farm. Is this number less than 10?* [Yes] *Is it a lot less?* [No] *Repeat with 6 counters for 6 pigs. Is this number less than 10?* [Yes]

 What numbers are greater than 5 and less than 10? [6, 7, 8, 9]

 **eTools Counters**
www.pearsonsuccessnet.com

Visual Learning

What do you think Mr. Brown is doing? [Counting the chickens] *Let's help him count. How many chickens are there?* [10] *How do you know?* [There are no empty squares in the ten-frame.]

1 Visual Learning

Set the Purpose Call children's attention to the **Visual Learning Bridge** at the top of the page. *In this lesson, you will compare numbers and decide if a number is greater than 10 or less than 10.*

2 Guided Practice

Remind children that they can compare numbers to 10.

Exercise 2
Error Intervention

If children have difficulty determining greater and less than 10,

then have them make a row of 10 counters and a row of the other number. Guide them to use one-to-one correspondence.

Sample answers for Exercises 1 and 2.

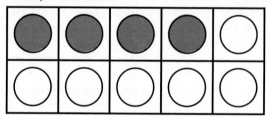

Do you understand? *How can you tell if a number is greater or less than 10 by using a ten-frame?* [Use counters to show the number. There will be extra counters if the number is greater than 10. There will be empty squares if the number is less than 10.]

Reteaching Place 10 chairs in a line. Have the class sort themselves by boys and girls and get into two lines on either side of the line of chairs. Then ask children to tell if their group has fewer than 10, more than 10, or the same as 10. Talk about whether the number of children in each group is greater than or less than 10.

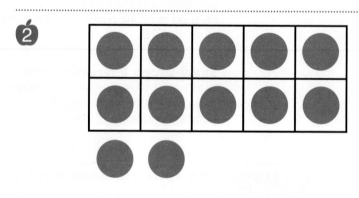

Directions Have children: **1.** Color counters to show a number that is a lot smaller than 10. **2.** Draw counters to sh number that is more than 10.

Topic 4 • Lesson 3

Let's count the chickens together. Point to each chicken as you count aloud with children. *Is 7 greater or less than 10?* [Less] *How do you know?* [There are 3 empty spaces in the ten-frame.]

Are there more than 10 chickens? How do you know? [Yes, there is 1 extra chicken below the ten-frame.]

Additional Activity

Greater Than or Less Than

🕐 15 min 👥

Materials Chart paper, marker, classroom objects

- Draw a large ten-frame on chart paper and place it on a table or on the floor.
- Use the ten-frame and classroom objects to show numbers greater and less than 10. For example, place 12 books on and below the ten-frame. *Are there more than 10 books?* [Yes] *How do you know?* [There are extra books below the ten-frame.]
- Repeat with objects such as paper cups to show a number less than 10.
- Ask volunteers to place other objects on and below the ten-frame. Classmates tell whether the number of objects is greater or less than 10 and how they know.

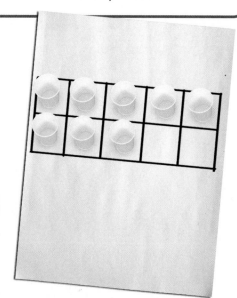

3 ❤️

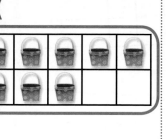

4

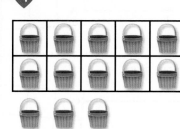

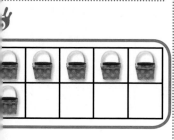

6 ☕

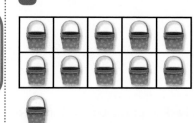

tions Have children circle each picture that shows fewer than 10.

seventy-two **72**

3 Independent Practice

Children circle the pictures that show fewer than 10 items and represent numbers less than 10. Children can use counters if needed.

Close

Essential Understanding You can use 10 as a benchmark to compare numbers. *Remember to count the number of objects to see if there are fewer than or more than 10.*

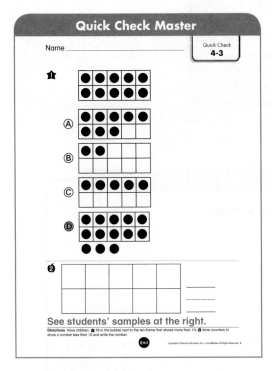

Formative Assessment

Use the **Quick Check** to assess children's understanding.

**ASSESSMENT**

Exercise 1 is worth 1 point.
Use the rubric to score Exercise 2.

Exercise 2
Attend to Precision Children should be able to draw 0–9 counters and write the number.

ELL Model Thinking Aloud For children who need additional help, have them point to and count the ten boxes in the ten-frame. Then have them put counters in some of the boxes and point to and count the counters.

Student Samples
3-point answer Children draw 0–9 counters in the ten-frame and write the number.

2-point answer Children draw 0–9 counters but do not write the number.

1-point answer Children draw more than 9 counters.

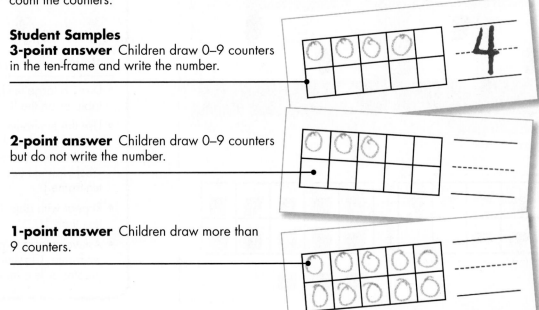

Prescription for Differentiated Instruction
Use children's work on the **Quick Check** to prescribe differentiated instruction.

Points	Prescription
0–2	Intervention
3	On-Level
4	Advanced

Differentiated Instruction

Intervention

Flash a Number

 10 min

Materials (per pair) Number Cards 0–10 (Teaching Tool 5)

- Tell children that when you flash a number, you want them to show that number on their fingers and say the number.
- Flash the number 8. Children hold up 8 fingers and say "8." *Are 8 fingers more than 10 or fewer than 10?* [Fewer than 10] *Are 8 fingers more than 5 or fewer than 5?* [More than 5]
- Repeat for all numbers 0 through 10.

Practice | **On-Level** | **Center Activity**

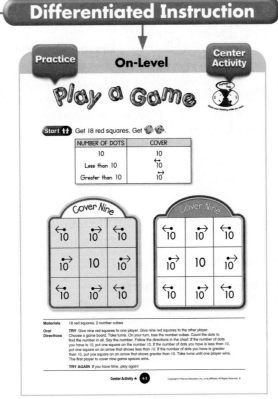

Practice | **Advanced** | **Center Activity**

ELL Partner Talk Listen for language that includes *greater than* and *less than* as a child compares a number to 10.

Leveled Homework

Reteaching Master

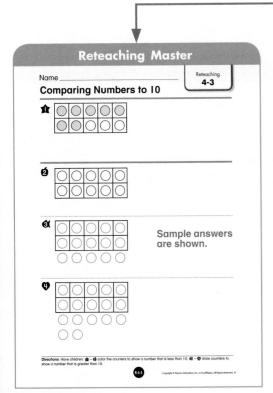

Also available in print

Practice Master

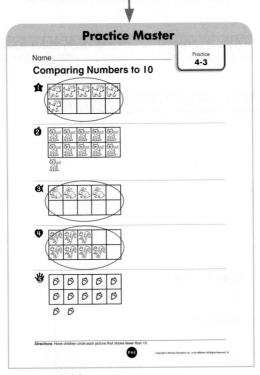

Also available in print

Enrichment Master

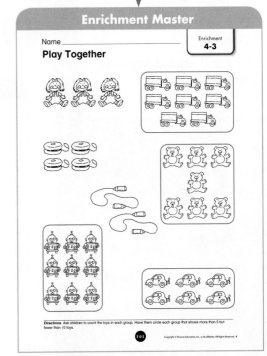

Also available in print

Domain
Counting and Cardinality

Cluster
Compare numbers.

Standards
K.CC.6 Identify whether the number of objects in one group is greater than, less than, or equal to the number of objects in another group, e.g., by using matching and counting strategies. Also **K.CC.7, K.OA.1**

Mathematical Practices
☑ Make sense of problems and persevere in solving them.

☑ Reason abstractly and quantitatively.

☑ Construct viable arguments and critique the reasoning of others.

○ Model with mathematics.

☑ Use appropriate tools strategically.

○ Attend to precision.

☑ Look for and make use of structure.

☑ Look for and express regularity in repeated reasoning.

1 More

 **Lesson Overview**

Objective	Essential Understanding	Vocabulary	Materials
Children will use counting to identify a number that is 1 more than another number.	*1 more than* expresses a relationship between two numbers.		Counters (or Teaching Tool 32)

© **PROFESSIONAL DEVELOPMENT**

Math Background

Research says ... Children learn that the relationships of one more than, two more than, one less than, and two less than are important for all numbers. However, these ideas are built on or connected to the same concepts for numbers less than 10 (John A. Van de Walle, 2004).

1 Daily Common Core Review

Daily Common Core Review

Name _____

Daily Common Core Review **4-4**

⭐

Ⓐ ♡♡♡

Ⓑ ♡♡♡♡

Ⓒ ♡♡♡♡♡

Ⓓ ♡♡♡♡♡♡

②

Ⓐ ▪▪▪▪▪ / ▪

Ⓑ ▪▪▪▪

Ⓒ ▪▪▪

Ⓓ ▪▪

Directions Have children mark the best answer. ⭐ Which picture shows a group of 6 hearts? ② Which picture shows a number of counters that is greater than 5?

Content Reviewed
Exercise 1   Count Objects
Exercise 2   Compare Numbers to 5

Also available in print

 30 min **Problem-Based Interactive Learning**

Overview Children count to identify how many in a group of objects, add 1 more to the group, and identify the number that is 1 more.

Focus How can you find the number that is 1 more than another number?

Materials Counters (Teaching Tool 32)

 **Set the Purpose** Remind children that they learned how to compare groups of objects. *You will learn to find numbers that are 1 more than other numbers in this lesson.*

Connect Ask 4 children to stand in a row. Have children say how many children are standing and write the number on the board. Then ask 5 children to stand in another row. Ask how many children are in that group and write the number. Ask which number is greater and which number is less.

Reason Quantitatively Remind children they have already learned how to count the items in a group and to compare two groups to each other.

Pose the Problem *Grandpa is making 6 sandwiches. Another person comes for lunch. He needs 1 more sandwich. How many sandwiches does Grandpa need now?* Have children share their ideas.

Model *Grandpa is making 6 sandwiches.* Count aloud as you place 6 counters on the ten-frame and have children do the same, placing one counter in each outline on the workmat. *Then he needs 1 more sandwich.* Place one more counter on the frame, count on, and say the number 7. Have children do the same. *7 is 1 more than 6.* Then have children trace and color 7 counters on their workmat. *We had 6 counters and we put 1 more counter in the frame. 7 is 1 more than 6. Let's trace the number 7 to show how many counters.* Repeat with this story: *Grandma makes 3 sandwiches and then makes 1 more.*

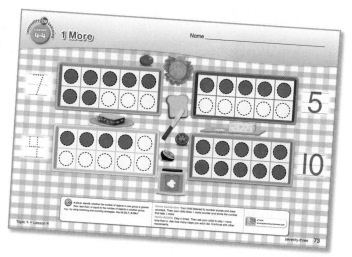

Use Math Manipulatives Make sure that children begin with the correct number of counters as you begin each story.

Small-Group Interaction Have partners work together to complete the student page as you tell other stories. *Grandma puts 4 tomatoes in a basket. Then she puts in 1 more tomato. How many tomatoes does she have now?* [5] *5 is 1 more than 4. Grandma collected 9 eggs. She found 1 more egg. How many eggs did she find?* [10] *10 is 1 more than 9.*

 I have 4 blocks. How many more blocks would I need to have 5 blocks? [1 more block]

 eTools **Counters** www.pearsonsuccessnet.com

Visual Learning

5

How many sandwiches do you see? Let's count to find out. Point to each sandwich as you count aloud with children. There are 5 sandwiches.

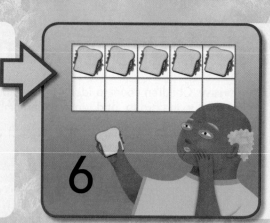

6

Grandpa is putting 1 more sandwich on the frame. How many sandwiches are there now? Let's count together to find out. [6] What number is 1 more than 5? [6]

1   Visual Learning

Set the Purpose Call children's attention to the **Visual Learning Bridge** at the top of the page. *In this lesson, you will learn about numbers that are 1 more than other numbers.*

2   Guided Practice

Remind children that they can count on to find 1 more.

Exercise 2
Error Intervention

If children forget to count 1 more,

then have them count aloud as they touch each counter to find the number.

Do you understand? *How do you know the number 4 is 1 more than 3?* [I can count on from 3 or use counters to show 1 more.]

Reteaching Call out a number, such as 3, and have children put that many cubes in a ten-frame. Then ask children to add 1 more cube. Help them finish the sentence: "3 and 1 more is..." [4]

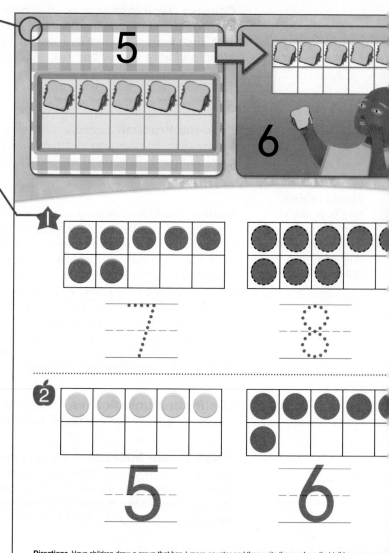

Directions Have children draw a group that has 1 more counter and then write the numbers that tell how many cou...

Topic 4 • Lesson 4

ELL
STRATEGY
Visual
Learning

Visual Learning Animation
www.pearsonsuccessnet.com or CD

9

How many sandwiches do you see? Let's count together to find out. Point to each sandwich as you count aloud with children. *There are 9 sandwiches.*

10

Grandpa is putting 1 more sandwich on the frame. How many sandwiches are there now? Let's count together to find out. [10] *What number is 1 more than 9?* [10]

9

10

Additional Activity

Add 1 More Clap

🕐 10 min 👬

- Have partners stand facing each other. Partner A rhythmically claps a selected number of times, from 1 to 9, counting each clap, such as: "1, 2, 3 claps." Partner B claps once more, saying, "And 1 more is 4 claps."

- Partners switch roles and repeat.

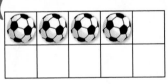

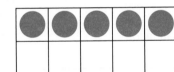

4   5

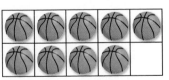

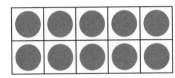

9   10

ctions Have children draw a group that has 1 more ball and then write the numbers that tell how many balls.

seventy-four   74

3 Independent Practice

Children draw 1 more ball in each group. Then they count and write the numbers that tell how many balls.

Close

Essential Understanding *1 more than* expresses a relationship between two numbers. *Remember to count objects to see if there is 1 more than in another group.*

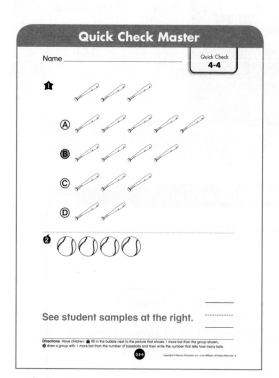

Formative Assessment

Use the **Quick Check** to assess children's understanding.

ASSESSMENT

Exercise 1 is worth 1 point.
Use the rubric to score Exercise 2.

Exercise 2
Reason Quantitatively Children should be able to draw a group with 1 more and write the number.

ELL **Rephrase** Rephrase a question or statement in a different way, rather than repeating it.

Student Samples
3-point answer Children draw 5 bats and write the number.

2-point answer Children draw 5 bats but do not write the number or write an incorrect number.

1-point answer Children draw an incorrect number of bats.

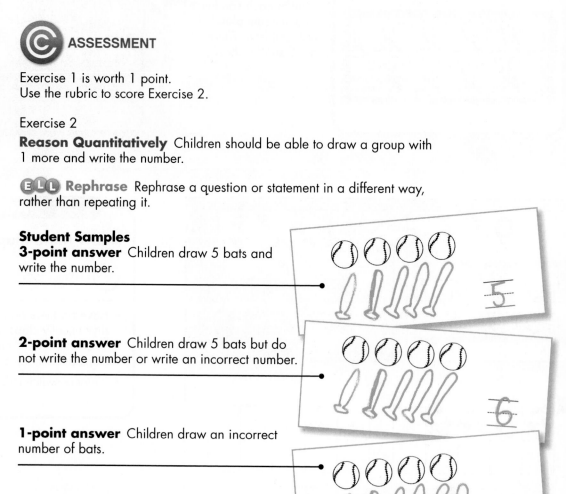

Prescription for Differentiated Instruction
Use children's work on the **Quick Check** to prescribe differentiated instruction.

Points	Prescription
0–2	Intervention
3	On-Level
4	Advanced

Differentiated Instruction

Intervention

Say 1 More

 10 min

Materials (per pair) Number Cards 1–5 (Teaching Tool 5), dried beans

- Stack the cards facedown. Model how to play. Turn over a card and say the number: 4, for example. Count out 4 beans and ask for 1 more. Count the beans again: *5 is 1 more than 4.*

- Partners take turns turning over a card, saying the number, and showing the correct number of beans. The child asks for 1 more, counts the beans, and tells the number that is 1 more.

ELL Report Back To check understanding, ask a child to repeat and complete this sentence: *9 is 1 more than* _____. [8]

Leveled Homework

Reteaching Master

Practice Master

Enrichment Master

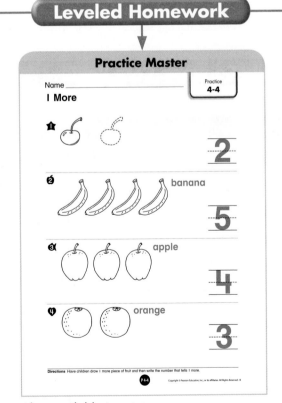

Also available in print

Also available in print

Also available in print

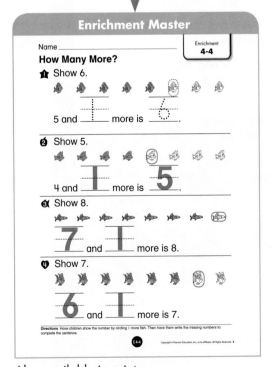

eTools **Counters**
www.pearsonsuccessnet.com

eTools **Counters**
www.pearsonsuccessnet.com

eTools **Counters**
www.pearsonsuccessnet.com

Common Core

Domain
Counting and Cardinality

Cluster
Compare numbers.

Standards
K.CC.6 Identify whether the number of objects in one group is greater than, less than, or equal to the number of objects in another group, e.g., by using matching and counting strategies. Also **K.CC.7, K.OA.1**

Mathematical Practices

☑ Make sense of problems and persevere in solving them.

☑ Reason abstractly and quantitatively.

○ Construct viable arguments and critique the reasoning of others.

○ Model with mathematics.

☑ Use appropriate tools strategically.

○ Attend to precision.

☑ Look for and make use of structure.

☑ Look for and express regularity in repeated reasoning.

1 Fewer

 **Lesson Overview**

Objective	Essential Understanding	Vocabulary	Materials
Children will use counting to identify a number that is 1 fewer than another number.	*1 fewer than* expresses a relationship between two numbers.		Number Cards 0–10 (Teaching Tool 5), Counters (Teaching Tool 32)

PROFESSIONAL DEVELOPMENT

Math Background

The overall concept of number is related to the basic concepts of *more, less,* and *same as.* Studies indicate that kindergarten children have more trouble using the words *less* or *fewer* than *more.* Frequently pair the word *more* with the word *less* in everyday classroom discussions.

1 Daily Common Core Review

Daily Common Core Review

Name _____

Daily Common Core Review 4-5

1 ⚞⚞⚞⚞

Ⓐ 🔲🔲

Ⓑ 🔲🔲🔲

Ⓒ 🔲🔲🔲🔲

Ⓓ 🔲🔲🔲🔲🔲

2 🍎🍎🍎🍎🍎🍎🍎🍎

Ⓐ 6
Ⓑ 7
Ⓒ 8
Ⓓ 9

Directions Have children mark the best answer. 1 Which picture shows the same number of cubes as boats? 2 Which number tells how many apples?

4-5

Copyright © Pearson Education, Inc., or its affiliates. All Rights Reserved. K

Also available in print

Content Reviewed

Exercise 1   Compare Quantities

Exercise 2   Use Numbers to Tell How Many

 30 min **Problem-Based Interactive Learning** *Hands-On Minds-On*

Overview Children will count to identify how many in a group of objects, remove 1 object, and identify the number that is 1 fewer.

Focus How can you find the number that is 1 fewer than another number?

Materials Number Cards 0–10 (Teaching Tool 5), Counters (Teaching Tool 32)

 **Engage**

Set the Purpose Remind children that they have learned how to compare groups of objects. *You will learn how to find numbers that show 1 fewer than other numbers in this lesson.*

Connect Display number cards in order from 0–10 on the board. Point to 2. *What number comes just before 2?* [1] Repeat with other numbers.

 MATHEMATICAL PRACTICES

Reason Quantitatively
Remind children they have learned how to count how many objects are in a group.

Pose the Problem *Jamal has 6 stuffed dinosaurs. He gives 1 dinosaur to a friend. How many dinosaurs does he have now?* Have children share their ideas.

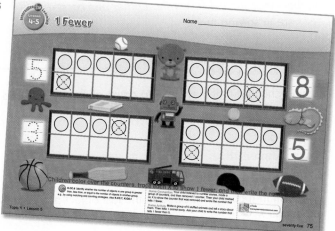

Model *Jamal has 6 stuffed dinosaurs.* Count aloud as you place 6 counters on the ten-frame and have children do the same on their workmats. *Then he gives 1 to his friend Thomas.* Remove one counter on the frame and count what is left. Guide children to do the same. *How many counters are there now?* [5] *5 counters is 1 fewer than 6 counters.* Then have them color over 5 counters and mark an X on the last counter (6th counter) to show the dinosaur that was given away. Repeat with another story about Jamal, who has 4 stuffed bears and gives 1 to his friend Keisha.

Small-Group Interaction Have partners work together to complete the student page as you tell another story. *Jamal has 9 stamps. He uses 1 stamp. How many stamps does he have now?* [8] *8 counters is 1 fewer than 9 counters.* Continue: *Jamal has 6 library books. He returns 1 book. How many books does he have now?*

 Extend

Write the numbers from 0–8 on the board in a row and circle the number 7. *I want to find the number that is 1 less than 7. What direction would I move to find the number that is 1 less than 7? Why?* [Left; the numbers get smaller.]

 eTools **Counters**
www.pearsonsuccessnet.com

How many toy dinosaurs are on the frame? Let's count together to find out. Point to each dinosaur as you count aloud with children. *There are 5 toy dinosaurs.*

Jamal is removing one dinosaur. Why is there an X on the fifth square? [It tells that one dinosaur was removed.] How many dinosaurs are there now? What number shows 1 fewer dinosaur than 5 dinosaurs? [4]

1 Visual Learning

Set the Purpose Call children's attention to the **Visual Learning Bridge** at the top of the page. *In this lesson, you will learn about numbers that show 1 fewer than other numbers.*

2 Guided Practice

Remind children that they have to count all the objects and then show a group with 1 fewer.

Exercise 2
Error Intervention

If children have trouble making a group that has 1 fewer,

then children can mark an X on the last object and count the objects without an X.

Do you understand? *How do you know that the number 8 is 1 fewer than 9?* [I can use counters to make groups, compare, and show 1 fewer.]

Reteaching Have five children line up and sing the song "Five in the Bed." At the end of each line, the child on the end leaves and sits down. As you repeat, point out what is happening. *There is 1 fewer child in line each time we sing.*

Directions Have children draw a group that has 1 fewer counter and then write the numbers that tell how many count

Topic 4 • Lesson 5

How many toy dinosaurs are on the frame? Let's count together to find out. Point to each dinosaur as you count aloud with children. *There are 10 toy dinosaurs.*

Why is there an X on the last square? [It tells that one dinosaur was removed.] *How many dinosaurs are there now? Let's count together. What number is 1 fewer dinosaur than 10 dinosaurs?* [9]

Directions Have children: **3.** Count the cups, draw a group that has 1 fewer cup, and then write the numbers that tell how many cups. **4.** Count the balls, draw groups that have 1 more and 1 fewer balls, and then write the numbers that tell how many balls.

seventy-six 76

Additional Activity

Disappearing Tiles

🕐 15 min 👬

Materials (per pair) 6 color tiles (or Teaching Tool 31)

- Partner A sets out 3 to 6 tiles. Partner B counts them, removes 1, and tells how many are left such as: "4 is 1 fewer than 5."

- Partner A removes 1 tile more and tells how many are left, saying, for example: "3 is 1 fewer than 4."

- The game continues in this way until no more tiles are left. Have children switch roles and repeat.

3   Independent Practice

Children draw a group with 1 fewer and write the numbers. Then they draw groups with 1 more and 1 fewer and write the numbers.

76A

Close

Essential Understanding *1 fewer than* expresses a relationship between two numbers. *Count objects to see if there is 1 fewer than in another group.*

ASSESSMENT

Exercise 1 is worth 1 point.
Use the rubric to score Exercise 2.

Exercise 2

Reason Quantitatively Children should be able to draw a group with 1 fewer and write the number.

ELL Rephrase Rephrase a question or statement in a different way, rather than simply repeating it.

Student Samples
3-point answer Children draw 2 scarves and write the number.

2-point answer Children draw 2 scarves but do not write the number or write an incorrect number.

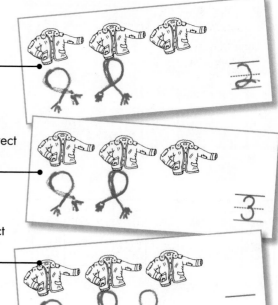

1-point answer Children draw an incorrect number of scarves.

Quick Check Master

Name _____

Quick Check
4-5

① 🧢🧢🧢🧢🧢

Ⓐ 🧢🧢🧢🧢🧢🧢

Ⓑ 🧢🧢🧢🧢🧢

Ⓒ 🧢🧢🧢🧢

Ⓓ 🧢🧢🧢

② 🧥🧥🧥

See student samples at the right.

Directions Have children: ★ fill in the bubble next to the picture that shows 1 fewer cap than the group shown; ② draw a group that has 1 fewer scarf than jackets and then write the number that tells how many scarves.

Copyright © Pearson Education, Inc., or its affiliates. All Rights Reserved. 4

**Formative** Assessment

Use the **Quick Check** to assess children's understanding.

Prescription for Differentiated Instruction
Use children's work on the **Quick Check** to prescribe differentiated instruction.

Points	Prescription
0–2	Intervention
3	On-Level
4	Advanced

Differentiated Instruction

Intervention

How Many Are There Now?

🕐 10 min 👤

Materials (per group) Connecting cubes in trains of 3 to 6 cubes

- Display a 3-cube train and have children write 3. Have a child count the cubes. Remove 1 cube. *How many cubes are there now?* [2] *2 is 1 fewer than 3.* Ask children to write the number of cubes left.

- Show other cube trains, asking children to write the numbers and to tell how many cubes are left when 1 is removed.

On-Level

Practice | On-Level | Center Activity

Advanced

Practice | Advanced | Center Activity

ELL Report Back To check understanding, ask a child to repeat and complete this sentence: *1 fewer than 7 is _____.* [6]

Leveled Homework

Reteaching Master

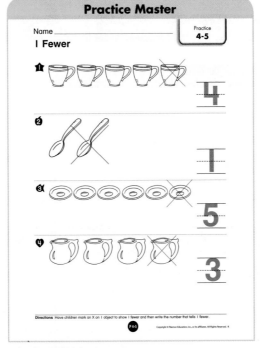

Practice Master

Enrichment Master

Also available in print

 eTools **Counters**
www.pearsonsuccessnet.com

Also available in print

 eTools **Counters**
www.pearsonsuccessnet.com

Also available in print

 eTools **Counters**
www.pearsonsuccessnet.com

© Common Core

Domain
Counting and Cardinality

Cluster
Compare numbers.

Standards
K.CC.6 Identify whether the number of objects in one group is greater than, less than, or equal to the number of objects in another group, e.g., by using matching and counting strategies. Also **K.CC.7, K.OA.1**

Mathematical Practices

☑ Make sense of problems and persevere in solving them.

☑ Reason abstractly and quantitatively.

○ Construct viable arguments and critique the reasoning of others.

○ Model with mathematics.

☑ Use appropriate tools strategically.

○ Attend to precision.

☑ Look for and make use of structure.

☑ Look for and express regularity in repeated reasoning.

2 More

 **Lesson Overview**

Objective	Essential Understanding	Vocabulary	Materials
Children will use counting to identify a number that is 2 more than another number.	*2 more than* expresses a relationship between two numbers.		Counters (Teaching Tool 32)

© **PROFESSIONAL DEVELOPMENT**

Math Background

This lesson builds on the concepts introduced in Lesson 4-4. Review these concepts by asking children questions such as, *How do you know if there is 1 more in a group of objects?*

1 Daily Common Core Review

Daily Common Core Review

Name _____

Daily Common Core Review **4-6**

Content Reviewed

Exercise 1   Count Objects

Exercise 2   Compare Quantities

Also available in print

 30 min # Problem-Based Interactive Learning

Overview Children will count to identify how many in a group of objects, make a group with 2 more, and identify the number that is 2 more.

Focus How can you find the number that is 2 more than another number?

Materials Counters (Teaching Tool 32)

Set the Purpose Remind children that they have learned how to add 1 more object to a group. *You will learn to find numbers that are 2 more than other numbers in this lesson.*

Connect Ask children to hold up 6 fingers. Write the number 6. Then ask them to show a group of fingers with 1 more. Write the number 7. Continue with other examples.

MATHEMATICAL PRACTICES

Reason Quantitatively Remind children they have learned how to count objects in a group.

Pose the Problem *Kim's grandma has 5 muffins on a plate. Then she puts 2 more on the plate. How many muffins are on the plate?* Have children share their ideas.

Model *Kim's grandma puts 5 muffins on a plate.* Count aloud as you place 5 counters on the ten-frame and have children do the same on their workmats. *She puts 2 more muffins on the plate.* Place 2 more counters on the frame, count on, and say the number 7. Have children do the same. *7 is 2 more than 5.* Then have children trace and color 7 counters on their workmats. *We had 5 counters and we put 2 more counters in the frame. 7 is 2 more than 5.* Then have children trace the number 7. Repeat with a story about Kim's grandma, who puts 7 apples in a bowl and then puts 2 more apples in the bowl. *9 is 2 more than 7.*

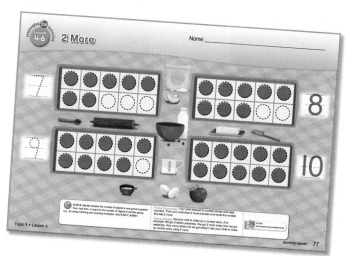

Use Math Manipulatives Make sure that children have the correct number of counters as you begin each story.

Small-Group Interaction Have partners work together to complete the student page as you tell stories about Peter. *Peter puts 6 toy cars on a table and later puts 2 more on the table. 8 is 2 more than 6. Peter puts 8 books on a table and later puts on 2 more. 10 is 2 more than 8.*

What number is 3 more than 5? How do you know? [8; I can count on from 5, or model 3 more than 5 on my workmat with counters.]

 eTools **Counters** www.pearsonsuccessnet.com

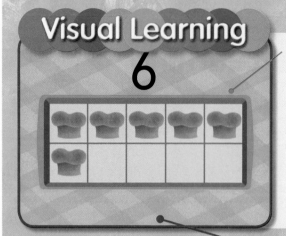

Visual Learning

6

How many muffins do you see? Let's count together to find out. Point to each muffin as you count aloud with children. *There are 6 muffins.*

8

Grandma is putting 2 more muffins on the frame. How many muffins are there now? Let's count together to find out. [8] *What number is 2 more than 6?* [8]

1 Visual Learning

Set the Purpose Call children's attention to the **Visual Learning Bridge** at the top of the page. *In this lesson, you will learn about numbers that are 2 more than other numbers.*

2 Guided Practice

Remind children that they can count on to find 2 more of a given number.

Exercise 2
Error Intervention

If children count 1 more instead of 2 more,

then have them use counters or point to each counter as they count aloud.

Do you understand? *How do you know the number 3 is 2 more than 1?* [I can count on from 1 or use counters to show 2 more.]

Reteaching Ask a volunteer to hop from 1 to 5 times. Have children count the number of hops. Next ask all the children to hop 2 more times than the volunteer. Ask how many times they hopped.

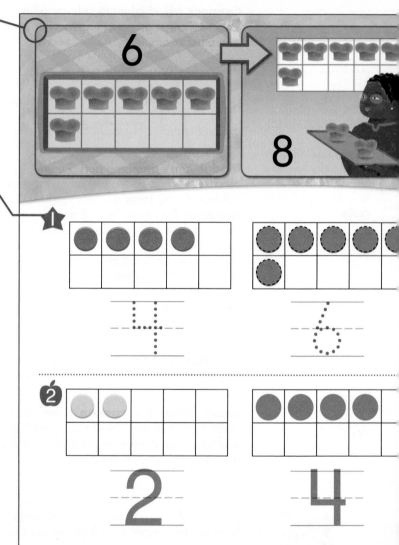

Directions Have children draw a group that has 2 more counters and then write the numbers that tell how many cou...

Topic 4 • Lesson 6

7

How many muffins do you see? Let's count together to find out. Point to each muffin as you count aloud with the children. *There are 7 muffins.*

9

Grandma is putting 2 more muffins on the frame. How many muffins are there now? Let's count together to find out. [9] *What number is 2 more than 7?* [9]

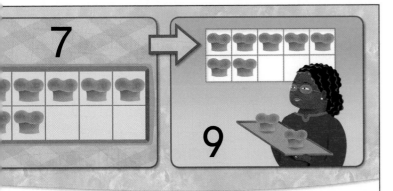

7

9

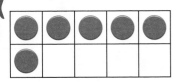 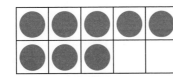

6

8

3

5

tions Have children: **3.** Count the counters, draw a group that has 2 more counters, and then write the numbers ell how many counters. **4.** Count the hearts, draw a group that has 2 more hearts, and then write numbers that tell nany hearts.

seventy-eight 78

Additional Activity

How Many More?

🕐 10 min 👫

Materials (per pair) 7 color tiles in one color

- Partner A selects from 1 to 5 color tiles and lays them on the table. Both children count them aloud together.
- Partner B closes his or her eyes while Partner A adds either 1 or 2 more counters to the group.
- Partner B opens his or her eyes and tells whether 1 or 2 more counters have been added to the original group.
- Children switch roles and repeat.

Children count and write how many. Then they draw 2 more objects in each group. They count and write the number.

Close

Essential Understanding *2 more than* expresses a relationship between two numbers. *Remember to count objects to see if there are 2 more than in another group.*

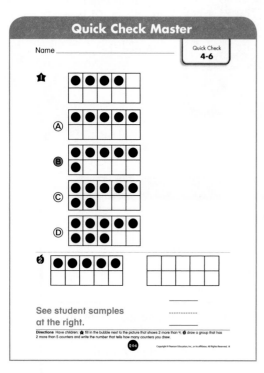

🌸 **Formative** Assessment

Use the **Quick Check** to assess children's understanding.

© **ASSESSMENT**

Exercise 1 is worth 1 point.
Use the rubric to score Exercise 2.

Exercise 2
Model with Mathematics Children should be able to draw a group with 2 more and write the number.

ELL Use Repetition Have children repeat key words, phrases, and sentences with you and after you.

Student Samples
3-point answer Children draw 7 counters and write the number.

2-point answer Children draw 7 counters but do not write the number or write an incorrect number.

1-point answer Children draw an incorrect number of counters.

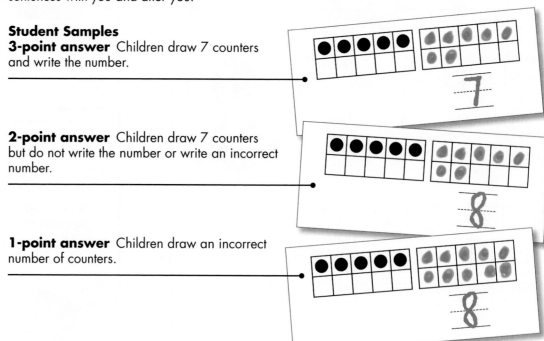

Prescription for Differentiated Instruction
Use children's work on the **Quick Check** to prescribe differentiated instruction.

Points	Prescription
0–2	Intervention
3	On-Level
4	Advanced

Differentiated Instruction

Intervention

May I Please Have More?

🕐 10 min 👥

Materials Crayons

- Have children gather in a circle. Give each child 1 to 5 crayons. Put extra crayons in the center.
- The first child counts his or her crayons aloud and asks: "May I please have 2 more?" The child takes 2 crayons from the center and describes the combination, such as: "7 is 2 more than 5."
- Continue until each child has asked for 2 more crayons.

Practice | **On-Level** | **Center Activity**

Math in *Motion*

Start ⬆⬆ Put 1 2 3 4 5 6 7 8 in a 🎁.

Say: "_____ is 2 more than _____."

Materials	Number tiles 1–8, paper bag
Oral Directions	TRY Take turns. Pick a tile from the bag. Look at the number. Then take that many steps with your partner. Count the steps aloud as you walk. Then take 2 more steps by yourself. Say, "_____ is 2 more than _____." Set the tile aside. Take turns until the bag is empty.
	TRY AGAIN If you have time, play again!

Center Activity ★ 4-6

Practice | **Advanced** | **Center Activity**

Math in *Motion*

Start ⬆⬆ Put 1 2 3 4 5 6 7 8 in a 🎁.

My number of steps is 2 more than what number?

Materials	Number tiles 1–8, paper bag
Oral Directions	TRY Take turns. Pick a tile from the bag. Look at the number. Hide the tile in your hand. Ask your partner to count as you take steps. Take the number of steps on your tile, and then take 2 more steps. Ask your partner, "My number of steps is 2 more than what number?" After you hear your partner's answer, show the tile. Tell why the number your partner said is the same or different. Set the tile aside. Take turns until the bag is empty.
	TRY AGAIN If you have time, play again!

Center Activity ★★ 4-6

ELL **Partner Talk** Listen for the words *2 more than* when a child asks, "My number of steps is *2 more than* which number?"

Leveled Homework

Reteaching Master

Name _____ | Reteaching 4-6

2 More

❶ 3 [ten-frame] 5

❷ 1 [ten-frame] 3

❸ 5 [ten-frame] 7

❹ 8 [ten-frame] 10

Directions Have children trace the number and color the counters to show that number. Then have them draw counters to show 2 more and write the number that tells 2 more.

R 4-6

Also available in print

Practice Master

Name _____ | Practice 4-6

2 More

❶ [4 balls] 6
ball ball

❷ [5 mittens] 7
mitten mitten

❸ [3 plates] 5
plate plate

❹ [8 hearts] 10
heart heart

Directions Have children draw 2 more objects and then write the number that tells 2 more.

P 4-6

Also available in print

Enrichment Master

Name _____ | Enrichment 4-6

How Many?

[house with windows, flowers, clouds]

Check drawings for accuracy.

How Many? | 2 More

[window] 2 | 4
[flower] 6 | 8
[cloud] 7 | 9

Directions Have children count the number of windows on the house and write the number that tells how many windows. Then have children draw 2 more windows on the house and write the number that tells how many. Have children repeat these steps for the flowers and the clouds.

E 4-6

Also available in print

DIGITAL
eTools **Counters**
www.pearsonsuccessnet.com

DIGITAL
eTools **Counters**
www.pearsonsuccessnet.com

DIGITAL
eTools **Counters**
www.pearsonsuccessnet.com

Domain
Counting and Cardinality

Cluster
Compare numbers.

Standards
K.CC.6 Identify whether the number of objects in one group is greater than, less than, or equal to the number of objects in another group, e.g., by using matching and counting strategies. Also **K.CC.7, K.OA.1**

Mathematical Practices

- ☑ Make sense of problems and persevere in solving them.
- ☑ Reason abstractly and quantitatively.
- ○ Construct viable arguments and critique the reasoning of others.
- ○ Model with mathematics.
- ☑ Use appropriate tools strategically.
- ○ Attend to precision.
- ☑ Look for and make use of structure.
- ☑ Look for and express regularity in repeated reasoning.

2 Fewer

 **Lesson Overview**

Objective	Essential Understanding	Vocabulary	Materials
Children will use counting to identify a number that is 2 fewer than another number.	*2 fewer than* expresses a relationship between two numbers.		Counters (Teaching Tool 32)

 PROFESSIONAL DEVELOPMENT

Math Background

This lesson builds on the concepts introduced in Lesson 5. Review these concepts by asking children questions such as, *How do you know if there is 1 fewer in a group of objects?*

1 Daily Common Core Review

Daily Common Core Review

Name _____

Daily Common Core Review
4-7

Directions: Have children: ★ fill in the bubble next to the vase that has the same number of flowers as the vase shown; ② count how many fish are in the tank and write how many.

Also available in print

Content Reviewed
Exercise 1   Compare Quantities
Exercise 2   Count How Many

 30 min **Problem-Based Interactive Learning** Hands-On Minds-On

Overview Children will count to identify how many in a group of objects, make a group with 2 fewer, and identify the number that is 2 fewer.

Focus How can you find the number that is 2 fewer than another number?

Materials Counters (or Teaching Tool 32)

 **Engage**

Set the Purpose Remind children that they have learned how to find 1 fewer object than a group of objects. *You will learn how to find numbers that show 2 fewer than other numbers in this lesson.*

Connect Ask 7 children to stand up. Write the number 7. Then ask 1 child to sit down. *What number is 1 fewer than 7?* Continue with other examples.

MATHEMATICAL
PRACTICES

Reason Quantitatively Remind children they learned how to count how many in a group of objects.

Pose the Problem *Spencer is at the pet store. He sees 8 birds. Two birds go away. What number is 2 fewer than 8?* Have children share their ideas.

Model Count aloud as you place 8 counters to represent the birds on the ten-frame and have children do the same on the workmat. *Then 2 birds leave.* Remove 2 counters and count what is left. Guide children to do the same. *How many counters are there now? 6 counters is 2 fewer than 8 counters.* Then have children color 8 counters and mark Xs on the last 2 (7th and 8th counters) to show the two birds that went away. Children then trace the number 6. Repeat with a story about Spencer, who sees 6 iguanas and then 2 go away. Children place 6 counters on the workmat, remove 2 of the counters, color 6 counters, mark Xs on the last 2 counters, and trace the number 4. *How many counters are there now?* [4] *4 counters is 2 fewer than 6 counters.*

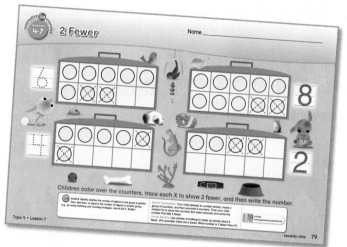

Small-Group Interaction Have partners work together to complete the student page as you tell another story. *The pet store has 10 guinea pigs. It sells 2 guinea pigs to Spencer. How many guinea pigs does the store have now?* [8] *8 counters is 2 fewer than 10.* Continue with this story: *The pet store has 4 bunnies. It sells 2 bunnies. How many bunnies does the store have now?* [2]

 Extend

What number is 3 fewer than 10? How do you know? [7; I can count back or model 3 fewer than 10 on a ten-frame.]

eTools **Counters**
www.pearsonsuccessnet.com

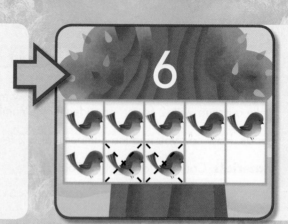

How many birds are on the frame? Let's count together to find out. Point to each bird as you count aloud with children. *There are 8 birds.*

Why are there two Xs on the last two birds? [It tells that two birds were removed.] How many birds are there now? Let's count together. What number shows 2 fewer birds than 8 birds? [6]

1 Visual Learning

Set the Purpose Call children's attention to the **Visual Learning Bridge** at the top of the page. *In this lesson, you will learn about numbers that show 2 fewer than other numbers.*

2 Guided Practice

Remind children that they will count the objects and then show a group with 2 fewer.

Exercise 2
Error Intervention

If children have trouble making a group with 2 fewer,

then have children mark Xs on the last 2 objects and count the objects without an X.

Do you understand? *How do you know the number 2 is 2 fewer than 4?* [I can use counters to make groups, compare, and show 2 fewer.]

Reteaching Display two lines of 5 connecting cubes each. Remove 2 cubes from one group. Match the cubes one-to-one with toothpicks. Point out the group with 2 fewer.

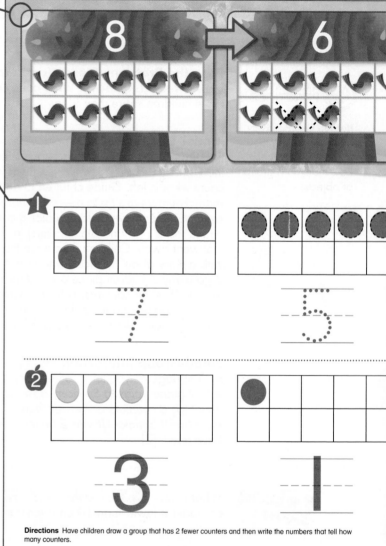

Directions Have children draw a group that has 2 fewer counters and then write the numbers that tell how many counters.

Topic 4 • Lesson 7

ELL
STRATEGY
Visual
Learning

Visual Learning Animation

www.pearsonsuccessnet.com or CD

How many birds are there? Let's count together to find out. Point to each bird as you count aloud with children. *There are 10 birds.*

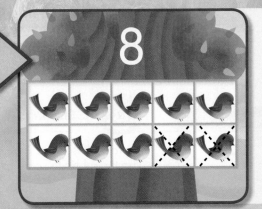

How many birds are removed? [2] *How can you tell?* [There are two Xs.] *How many birds are there now? Let's count together. What number is 2 fewer than 10?* [8] *How can we check our answer?* Count aloud with children.

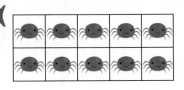

10   8

 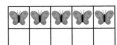 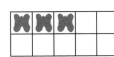

7   5   3

Additional Activity

Picturing 1 and 2 Fewer

🕐 10 min 🧍

Materials Construction paper, crayons

- Model folding the paper vertically to make 3 equal sections. Ask the child to draw 6 objects in the first section.

- In the other sections, the child draws the same objects and marks Xs to show 1 fewer and 2 fewer than 6.

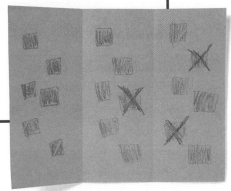

ctions Have children: **3.** count the spiders, draw a group that has 2 fewer spiders, and then write the numbers that
ow many spiders. **4.** count the butterflies, draw groups that have 2 more and 2 fewer butterflies, and then write the
bers that tell how many butterflies.

eighty   80

3 Independent Practice

Children count and write the number. They draw a group with 2 fewer and write the number. Then they draw groups with 2 more and 2 fewer and write the numbers.

80A

Close

Essential Understanding *2 fewer than* expresses a relationship between two numbers. *Remember to count objects to see if there are 2 fewer than in another group.*

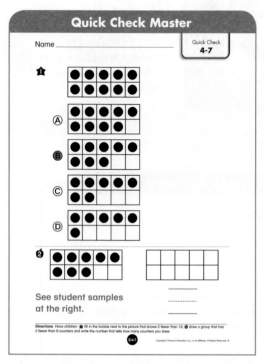

Formative Assessment

Use the **Quick Check** to assess children's understanding.

ⒸＡＳＳＥＳＳＭＥＮＴ

Exercise 1 is worth 1 point.
Use the rubric to score Exercise 2.

Exercise 2

Attend to Precision Children should be able to draw a group with 2 fewer and write the number.

ELL Use Repetition Have children repeat key words, phrases, and sentences with you and after you.

Student Samples
3-point answer Children draw 6 counters and write the number.

2-point answer Children draw 6 counters but do not write the number or write an incorrect number.

1-point answer Children draw an incorrect number of counters.

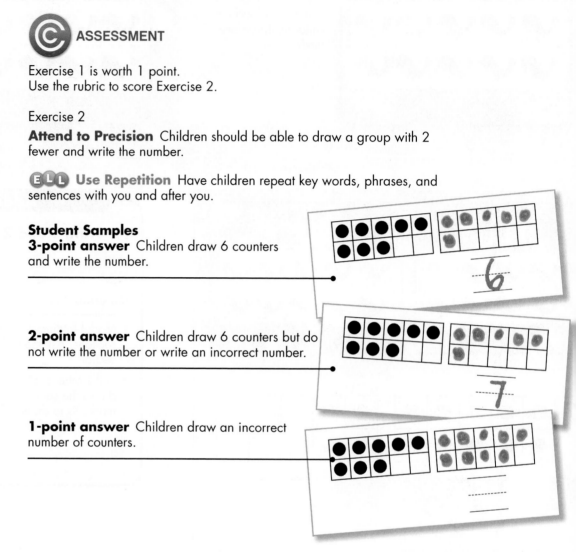

Prescription for Differentiated Instruction
Use children's work on the **Quick Check** to prescribe differentiated instruction.

Points	Prescription
0–2	Intervention
3	On-Level
4	Advanced

Differentiated Instruction

Intervention

Cover 1 or 2

 10 min

Materials Counters (Teaching Tool 32)

- Count out 4 counters and write 4. Cover 1 counter. *Now there is 1 fewer.* Count again. *3 is 1 fewer than 4.* Cross out the 4, write 3, and have children say, "3 is 1 fewer than 4."

- Count out 3 counters and then cover 2. *Now there are 2 fewer.* Repeat the activity, having children say, "1 is 2 fewer than 3."

- Partners repeat the activity, describing each situation.

On-Level

Practice | **On-Level** | **Center Activity**

Listen and Learn

Start ↑↑ Count the things in each group.

Materials None

Oral Directions **TRY** Take turns. Choose a corner of the game board. Count the animals or objects in each group in that corner. Point to the group that shows 2 fewer. Tell why.

TRY AGAIN If you have time, play again! This time, make some taps with your foot. Ask your partner to make 2 fewer taps.

Center Activity ★ ● 4-7 ● Copyright © Pearson Education, Inc., or its affiliates. All Rights Reserved.

Advanced

Practice | **Advanced** | **Center Activity**

Listen and Learn

Start ↑↑ Count the things in each group.

Materials None

Oral Directions **TRY** Take turns. Point to a group of animals or objects. Count how many. Tell how many animals or objects would be in the group if it had 2 fewer.

TRY AGAIN If you have time, play again! If you have more time, find a group of objects in your classroom. Tell how many there would be if the group had 2 fewer.

Center Activity ★★ ● 4-7 ● Copyright © Pearson Education, Inc., or its affiliates. All Rights Reserved.

ELL Report Back To check understanding, ask a child to repeat and complete this sentence: *A way to find 2 fewer than a number is to _____.* [Count back 2]

Leveled Homework

Reteaching Master

Name _____ | Reteaching **4-7**

2 Fewer

① 5 ▢▢▢▢▢ 3
② 7 ▢▢▢▢▢ 5
③ 9 ▢▢▢▢▢ 7
④ 8 ▢▢▢▢▢ 6

Directions Have children count the counters and trace the number. Then have them mark Xs on 2 counters to show 2 fewer and write the number that tells 2 fewer.

R 4-7 Copyright © Pearson Education, Inc., or its affiliates. All Rights Reserved. K

Also available in print

 eTools **Counters** www.pearsonsuccessnet.com

Practice Master

Name _____ | Practice **4-7**

2 Fewer

① / / / / / ✗✗ 4
② ⌣⌣⌣⌣⌣✗✗ 5
③ ◯✗✗ 1
④ 🍴🍴🍴✗✗ 3
✋ 🥄🥄🥄🥄🥄✗✗ 6

Directions Have children mark an X on 2 objects to show 2 fewer and then write the number that tells 2 fewer.

P 4-7 Copyright © Pearson Education, Inc., or its affiliates. All Rights Reserved. K

Also available in print

 eTools **MindPoint Quiz Show** Comparing Numbers 0 to 10 www.pearsonsuccessnet.com

Enrichment Master

Name _____ | Enrichment **4-7**

How Many Fewer?

① 2 fewer than 5 is 3.
② 2 fewer than 8 is 6.
③ 2 fewer than 7 is 5.
④ 2 fewer than 6 is 4.

Directions Have children mark Xs on 2 dogs to show 2 fewer and then write the numbers to complete the sentence.

E 4-7 Copyright © Pearson Education, Inc., or its affiliates. All Rights Reserved. K

Also available in print

 eTools **Counters** www.pearsonsuccessnet.com

Common Core

Domain

Counting and Cardinality

Cluster

Know number names and the count sequence.

Standards

K.CC.2 Count forward beginning from a given number within the known sequence (instead of having to begin at 1). Also **K.CC.4.c**

Mathematical Practices

✔ Make sense of problems and persevere in solving them.

☑ Reason abstractly and quantitatively.

○ Construct viable arguments and critique the reasoning of others.

○ Model with mathematics.

☑ Use appropriate tools strategically.

○ Attend to precision.

☑ Look for and make use of structure.

☑ Look for and express regularity in repeated reasoning.

Ordering Numbers Through 10

 **Lesson Overview**

Objective	Essential Understanding	Vocabulary	Materials
Children will order numbers from 0 through 10 in sequence.	There is a specific order to the set of whole numbers.		Number Cards 0–10 (Teaching Tool 5), glue, blunt-tipped scissors

© **PROFESSIONAL DEVELOPMENT**

Math Background

Make the connection between comparing numbers and ordering numbers. Help children see that when we count, the next number is always 1 more than the current number. The number before the current number is always 1 less.

1 Daily Common Core Review

Daily Common Core Review

Name _____

Daily Common Core Review
4-8

⭐ 🐶🌍🎖️🌈
🏈💜🦁🖼️

Ⓐ 7

Ⓑ 8

Ⓒ 9

Ⓓ 10

②

Ⓐ ☆☆☆☆☆☆☆

Ⓑ ☆☆☆☆☆☆

Ⓒ ☆☆☆☆☆

Ⓓ ☆☆☆☆

Directions Have children mark the best answer. ⭐ Which number tells how many stickers? ② Which picture shows fewer than 5 stars?

Content Reviewed

Exercise 1 Use Numbers to Tell How Many

Exercise 2 Compare Quantities

Also available in print

 30 min **Problem-Based Interactive Learning**

Overview Children will use number cards to show the order of numbers from 0–10 in sequence.

Focus Which numbers do you know that come after 5?

Materials (per child) Number Cards 0–10 (Teaching Tool 5), glue, blunt-tipped scissors

Set the Purpose Remind children that they learned how to compare numbers. *You will learn the order of the numbers 0 to 10 in this lesson.*

Connect *Let's use our fingers to count to 10.* Have children hold up their fingers as they count to 10 in sequential order.

 MATHEMATICAL **PRACTICES**

Reason Abstractly
Ask children how comparing numbers can help them determine the order in which they come.

Pose the Problem Tape the number cards 0, 5, 2, 4, 1, and 3 on the board. *Angela and Carlos are playing a game. They need to put these number cards in order: 0, 5, 2, 4, 1, 3. How can they do that?* Have children share their ideas before modeling the solution.

Model Distribute number cards to children. *Let's look at our number cards: 0, 2, 5, 4, 1, 3. Let's think about how we count. What number in this group comes first? That's right, 0. Let's put 0 in the first box on the workmat.* Model and have children do the same. *What number comes after 0?* Establish the order of the numbers through discussion. *Let's put 1 after 0.* Continue with 2, 3, 4, and 5. *Let's look at our numbers and say them together: 0, 1, 2, 3, 4, and 5. What number comes just after 2?* [3] *What number comes before 1?* [0] After children have the cards in order, have them glue the number cards in the boxes in correct sequence. *How do you know the numbers are in the correct order?* [Each number is one more than the number before it.]

Peer Questioning Have partners work together as you tell another story to order the rest of the cards. As they work, have children ask each other questions about what they are doing such as: "Which number comes after 5?" and "What number follows 6?" Children glue the rest of the numbers in the correct sequence. Then have them read the numbers aloud in the correct sequence.

Have partners use their number cards to play a game of *What Number Is Missing?* Model the game with a volunteer. Place the number cards for 6, 7, 9, and 10 in a row. *What number is missing in this group of numbers 6, 7, 9, 10?* [8] Partners then take turns playing the game.

DIGITAL eTools **Counters**
www.pearsonsuccessnet.com

Visual Learning

What numbers do you see? Let's say the numbers aloud. Point to each number as you say them aloud. [0, 1, 2] Are they in order? [Yes]

What numbers do you see? [3, 4, 5] Are they in order? [Yes] What number do you think comes next? [6] Why? [6 is one more than 5.]

1 Visual Learning

Set the Purpose Call children's attention to the **Visual Learning Bridge** at the top of the page. *In this lesson, you will learn the order of the numbers 0 to 10.*

2 Guided Practice

Remind children that they can order numbers from 0 to 10.

Error Intervention

If children have difficulty ordering numbers,

then have them use connecting cube towers to model each number.

Do you understand? *Which number comes before 6? [5] Which number comes after 3? [4]*

Reteaching Put randomly arranged classroom objects on trays in quantities of 0 through 10, arranged. Have children count the objects on each tray and label it with a number card. Then they line up trays in order from 0 to 10.

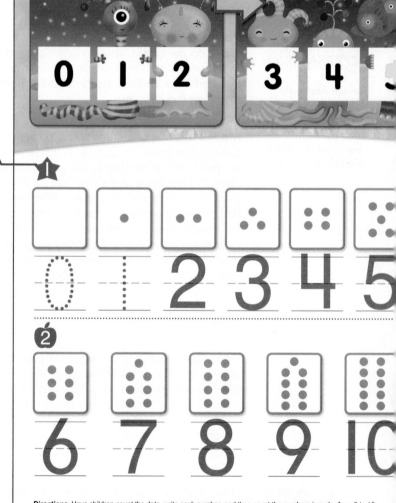

Directions Have children count the dots, write each number, and then count the numbers in order from 0 to 10.

Topic 4 • Lesson 8

What numbers do you see? Say them aloud. [6, 7, 8] How do you know they are in order? [Each number is one more than the number before it.]

What numbers do you see? Say them aloud. [9, 10] Which number is last? [10] Are they in order? [Yes] How do you know? [10 is one more than 9.]

6 7 8 9

3 4 5 6

7 8 9 10

ctions Have children write the numbers in the correct order.

eighty-two 82

3 **Independent Practice**

Children write the numbers in the correct order.

82A

Close

Essential Understanding There is a specific order to the set of whole numbers.
Remember that counting helps you find the next number in order.

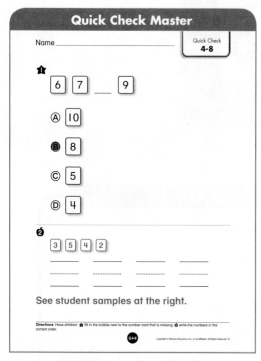

Formative
Assessment

Use the **Quick Check** to assess children's understanding.

ASSESSMENT

Exercise 1 is worth 1 point.
Use the rubric to score Exercise 2.

Exercise 2
Model with Mathematics Children should be able to write and order the numbers correctly.

ELL **Rephrase** Use the words *before* and *after* to help children order numbers. *What number comes before 6? What number comes after 4?*

Student Samples
3-point answer Children write the numbers correctly and in the correct order.

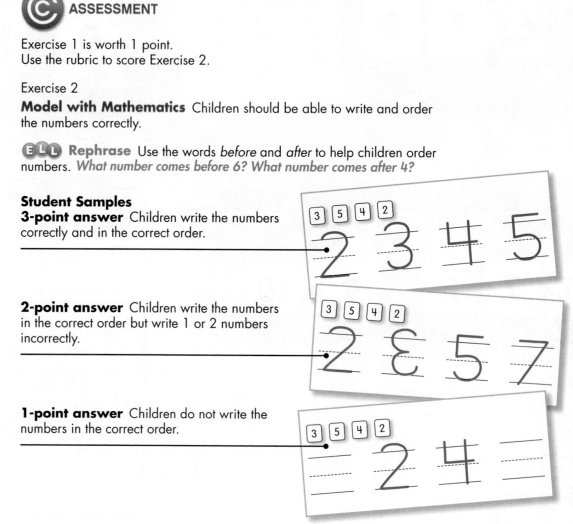

2-point answer Children write the numbers in the correct order but write 1 or 2 numbers incorrectly.

1-point answer Children do not write the numbers in the correct order.

Prescription for Differentiated Instruction
Use children's work on the **Quick Check** to prescribe differentiated instruction.

Points	Prescription
0–2	Intervention
3	On-Level
4	Advanced

Differentiated Instruction

Intervention

Space Shuttle Launch

 10 min

- Ask Partner A to crouch down and pretend to be an astronaut in the space shuttle getting ready for liftoff.
- Partner B pretends to be Mission Control and counts the shuttle launch backward from 10 to 0.
- At 0, Partner A jumps up as if launching.
- Partners switch roles and repeat.

Practice | **On-Level** | **Center Activity**

Practice | **Advanced** | **Center Activity**

ELL Partner Talk Listen for the words *before* and *after*. For example, a child might say, "We should put 7 *before* 8, and 9 comes *after* 8."

Leveled Homework

Reteaching Master

Name _____ Reteaching **4-8**

Ordering Numbers Through 10

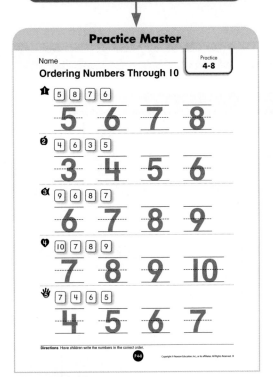

Also available in print

Practice Master

Name _____ Practice **4-8**

Ordering Numbers Through 10

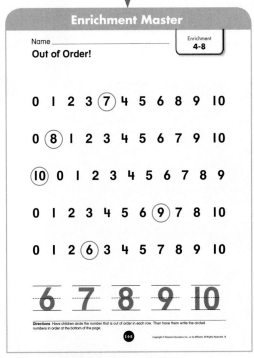

Also available in print

Enrichment Master

Name _____ Enrichment **4-8**

Out of Order!

Also available in print

eTools **Counters**
www.pearsonsuccessnet.com

eTools **Counters**
www.pearsonsuccessnet.com

eTools **Counters**
www.pearsonsuccessnet.com

82C

Ordering Numbers on a Number Line

 **Lesson Overview**

Objective	Essential Understanding	Vocabulary	Materials
Children will use a number line to count numbers 0 to 10 in order.	Numbers can be shown by a unique point on the number line. The distance between any two consecutive whole numbers on a given number line is always the same.	**order** **number line** **forward** **backward**	Number Cards 0–10 (from Teaching Tool 5), glue

Common Core

Domain
Counting and Cardinality

Cluster
Know number names and the count sequence.

Standard
K.CC.2 Count forward beginning from a given number within the known sequence (instead of having to begin at 1).

Mathematical Practices

☑ Make sense of problems and persevere in solving them.

☑ Reason abstractly and quantitatively.

○ Construct viable arguments and critique the reasoning of others.

○ Model with mathematics.

☑ Use appropriate tools strategically.

☑ Attend to precision.

☑ Look for and make use of structure.

○ Look for and express regularity in repeated reasoning.

PROFESSIONAL DEVELOPMENT

Math Background

To help children remember the counting order for numbers 0 through 10, they can refer to a number line. This shows them how the numbers 0 to 10 are related to one another. It is a concrete way for children to begin to learn how to compare and order numbers, which they will do in later grades.

1 Daily Common Core Review

Daily Common Core Review

Name _____

Daily Common Core Review **4-9**

Content Reviewed

Exercise 1 Same As

Exercise 2 Reading and Writing 6

Exercise 3 Reading and Writing 9

Also available in print

 **30 min** # Problem-Based Interactive Learning *Hands-On Minds-On*

Overview Children will use a number line to count and order numbers from 0 to 10.

Focus How can you use a number line to help count from 0 to 10?

Materials (per child) Number Cards 0 to 10 (from Teaching Tool 5), glue

Vocabulary order, number line, forward, backward

 **Engage**

Set the Purpose Remind children that they have learned how to count up to 10. *You will learn another way to count from 0 to 10.*

Connect Have children hold up one finger at a time as they count from 1 to 10.

 **MATHEMATICAL PRACTICES**

Use Appropriate Tools Remind children they already know the numbers 0–10 and what order they come in.

Academic Vocabulary Write the numbers from 0 to 10 in a row on the board. Count the numbers aloud with children and explain that the numbers are in **order**. Point out that a **number line** looks something like the row of numbers except that it is a line with evenly spaced marks and labeled with the numbers in order.

Pose the Problem *The empty boxes have missing numbers. How can you use a number line to find the missing numbers and show the numbers in order from 0 to 10?* Have children share ideas before using a number line.

Model Point out the empty boxes between 1 and 4. *We can use a number line to find out which numbers are missing. Let's count to 4 using the number line.* Point to each number on the number line and have children do the same as you count aloud together from 0 to 4. *What number did we say just after we said 1?* [2] Glue the number 2 in the box as children do the same on their student page. *What number did we say just before we said 4?* [3] Glue the number 3 in the box as children do the same on their student page. Point to the empty box just after the number 4. *How can we find out which number comes just after 4?* [Look at the number line and count.] Point and count aloud to 5. Have children follow you as you glue the number 5 in the box.

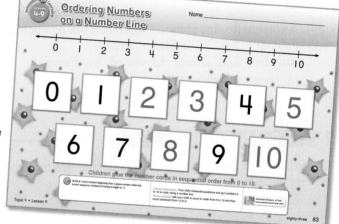

Use Math Manipulatives Make sure children glue the correct number in each box.

Small-Group Interaction Ask another question about number order: *How can we find out what number comes before 9?* Have children work in pairs as they count on the number line to 9, and then glue 8 in the box. Repeat for the number after 9. Finally, have children count aloud **forward** from 0 to 10 and then **backward** from 10 to 0. *When we count forward, we count from 0 to 10. When we count backward, we count from 10 to 0.*

 Extend Have children make a dot-to-dot drawing and label the dots from 1–10 in order, give it to a partner, and have the partner draw the picture.

 **eTools Counters** www.pearsonsuccessnet.com

Visual Learning

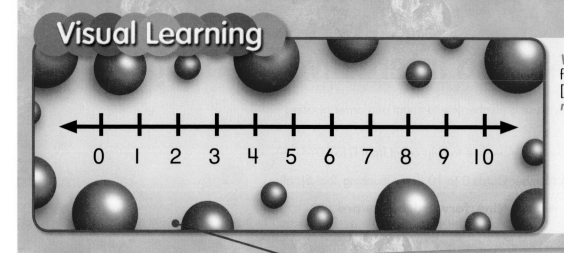

What do you see in this box? [A number line from 0 to 10] *How are the numbers arranged?* [In order from smallest to biggest] *What number comes after 3?* [4] *Before 7?* [6]

1 Visual Learning

Set the Purpose Call children's attention to the **Visual Learning Bridge** at the top of the page. *In this lesson, you will learn to use a number line to order numbers to 10.*

 Animated Glossary Children can see highlighted words defined in the Online Student Edition.

number line, **order**, **forward**, **backward**

www.pearsonsuccessnet.com

2 Guided Practice

Remind children that they can use the number line to find and write missing numbers.

Error Intervention

If children have trouble remembering the order of numbers,

then have them count quietly to themselves and refer to the number line at the top of the page.

Do you understand? *What is a number line?* [A line of numbers in order from smallest to biggest] *How can you use a number line to find missing numbers?* [Count on the number line to figure out which number we say before or after a missing number.]

Reteaching Draw a number line on the board. Leave one space blank. Give clues using the words *before* and *after*. For example, leave 7 blank and give clues such as: *It comes before 8. It comes after 6. What is the number?* Repeat several times with different missing numbers.

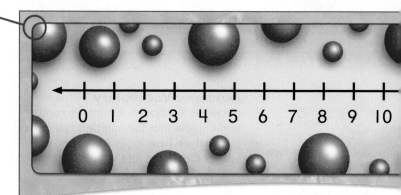

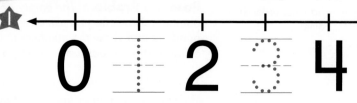

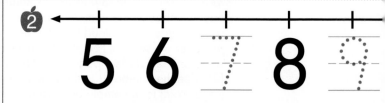

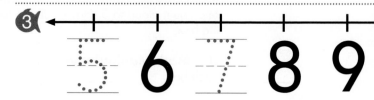

Directions Have children trace each missing number.

Topic 4 • Lesson 9

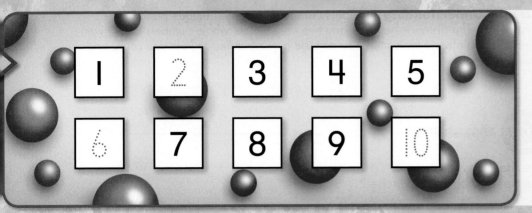

What do you see in this box? [Number cards, some with numbers, some with dotted numbers] *How is this box like the first one? How is it different?* [It shows some numbers in order; it is missing some numbers.] *How can you use the number line to help fill in the missing numbers?* [Count the numbers on the number line, and then write the missing numbers.] Have children trace the dotted numbers.

Additional Activity

Tray Round Up

🕐 10 min 👥

Materials Number line for 0–10 displayed on board; (per group) 11 small trays or pieces of cardboard, small classroom objects, Number Cards 0–10 (Teaching Tool 5)

• Put collections of classroom objects—such as paper clips, pencils, and crayons—in trays in quantities of 0 to 10 in random order.

• Have children count the objects on each tray, label the collection with the correct number card, and then work together to order the trays from 0 to 10.

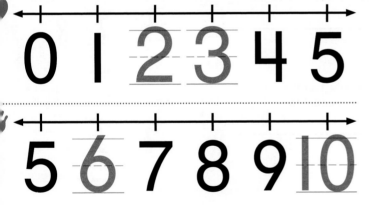

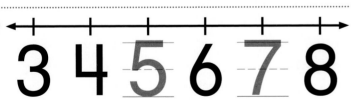

tions Have children write the missing numbers in each number line.

eighty-four **84**

3 Independent Practice

Children write the missing numbers on the number lines. Children can refer to the number line at the top of the page if they need help.

Close

Essential Understanding Numbers can be shown by a unique point on the number line. The distance between any two consecutive whole numbers on a given number line is always the same. *You can use a number line to help you count and order numbers.*

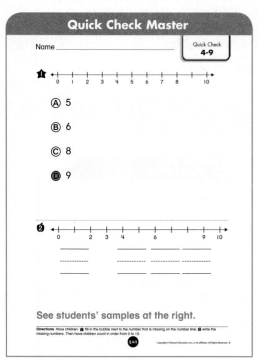

Formative
Assessment

Use the **Quick Check** to assess children's understanding.

ASSESSMENT

Exercise 1 is worth 1 point.
Use the rubric to score Exercise 2.

Exercise 2

Use Appropriate Tools Children should be able to order numbers to 10 on a number line.

ELL Use Repetition For children who need additional help following directions, have them repeat key words and phrases before beginning their work.

Student Samples
3-point answer Children write the missing numbers correctly and count to 10 correctly.

2-point answer Children write only 3 of the missing numbers correctly and do not count to 10 correctly.

1-point answer Children write only 1 of the missing numbers correctly and do not count to 10 correctly.

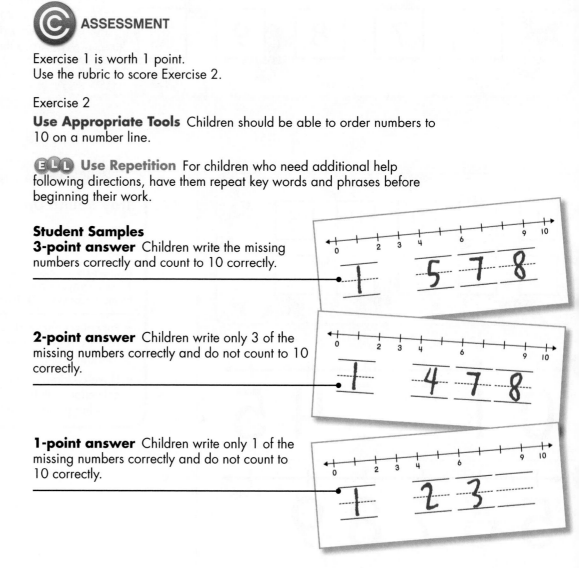

Prescription for Differentiated Instruction
Use children's work on the **Quick Check** to prescribe differentiated instruction.

Points	Prescription
0–2	**Intervention**
3	**On-Level**
4	**Advanced**

Differentiated Instruction

Intervention

Line 'Em Up

 10 min

Materials Number line for 0–10 drawn on the board; (per pair) 11 large index cards, crayons, yarn, tape

- Have partners make a set of number cards for the numbers 0 to 10. On each card, children write a number and draw simple pictures of objects to represent the number. For example, a child can draw an apple on the number card 1 or 2 oranges on the 2 card. *How many objects should you draw on the 0 card?* [No objects]

- Partners order their number cards and then make a number line by fastening the cards to a piece of yarn or string.

- Have partners compare their number line to the one on the board.

Practice — On-Level — Center Activity

Helping Hands ✋

Start ↑↑ Put 1 2 3 4 5 6 7 8 9 in a 🎁

Get 1 red square.

0 1 2 3 4 5 6 7 8 9 10

Materials Number tiles 1–9, a bag for the tiles, 1 red square

Oral Directions TRY Take turns. Pick a tile. Use the corner of the red square to point to that number on the number line. Ask your partner to count in order from 0 up to your number on the number line. Set the tile aside. Take turns until the bag of tiles is empty.

TRY AGAIN If you have time, play again! This time count back from your number to 0.

Center Activity ★ 4-9   Copyright © Pearson Education, Inc., or its affiliates. All Rights Reserved. K

Practice — Advanced — Center Activity

Helping Hands ✋

Start ↑↑ Put 0 1 2 3 4 5 6 7 8 9 in a 🎁

Get 1 red square.

0 1 2 3 4 5 6 7 8 9 10

Materials Number tiles 0–9, a bag for the tiles, 1 red square

Oral Directions TRY Take turns. Pick a tile. Use the corner of the red square to point to that number on the number line. Ask your partner to count in order from 0 up to your number on the number line. Set the tile aside. Take turns until the bag of tiles is empty.

TRY AGAIN If you have time, play again! This time, count back from 10 to 0.

Center Activity ★★ 4-9   Copyright © Pearson Education, Inc., or its affiliates. All Rights Reserved. K

ELL Report Back To check understanding, ask a child to repeat and complete this sentence: *On a number line, the four numbers that come after 6 are _____.* [Seven, eight, nine, ten]

Leveled Homework

Reteaching Master

Name _____   Reteaching 4-9
Using a Number Line

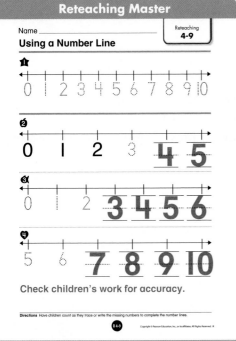

Check children's work for accuracy.

Directions Have children count as they trace or write the missing numbers to complete the number lines.

R 4-9   Copyright © Pearson Education, Inc., or its affiliates. All Rights Reserved. K

Also available in print

Practice Master

Name _____   Practice 4-9
Using a Number Line

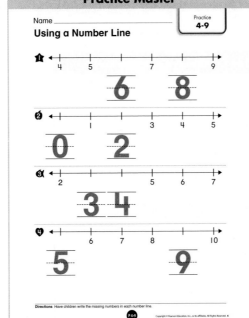

Directions Have children write the missing numbers in each number line.

P 4-9   Copyright © Pearson Education, Inc., or its affiliates. All Rights Reserved. K

Also available in print

Enrichment Master

Name _____   Enrichment 4-9
What Flies in the Sky?

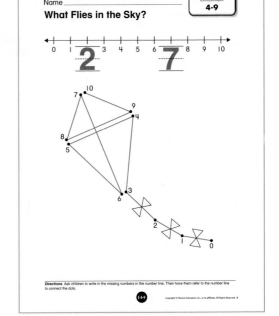

Directions Ask children to write in the missing numbers in the number line. Then have them refer to the number line to connect the dots.

E 4-9   Copyright © Pearson Education, Inc., or its affiliates. All Rights Reserved. K

Also available in print

 DIGITAL eTools **Counters** www.pearsonsuccessnet.com

 DIGITAL eTools **Counters** www.pearsonsuccessnet.com

DIGITAL eTools **Counters** www.pearsonsuccessnet.com

Problem Solving: Use Objects

Domain
Counting and Cardinality

Cluster
Compare numbers.

Standard
K.CC.7 Compare two numbers between 1 and 10 presented as written numerals.

Mathematical Practices

☑ Make sense of problems and persevere in solving them.

☑ Reason abstractly and quantitatively.

○ Construct viable arguments and critique the reasoning of others.

○ Model with mathematics.

☑ Use appropriate tools strategically.

○ Attend to precision.

☑ Look for and make use of structure.

○ Look for and express regularity in repeated reasoning.

 **Lesson Overview**

Objective	Essential Understanding	Vocabulary	Materials
Children will solve problems by using counters to show 1 more and 2 more.	Some problems can be solved by using objects to act out the actions in the problem.		Counters or Teaching Tool 32

 **PROFESSIONAL DEVELOPMENT**

Math Background

Ask questions to help children understand the relationship between counters and the objects that they are counting or adding. *How do you* *know how many counters to use? How many counters for "one more"? How many counters in all?*

1 Daily Common Core Review

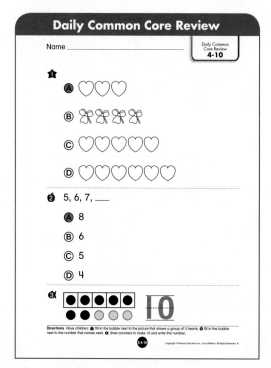

Content Reviewed

Exercise 1   Count Objects

Exercise 2   Count Up

Exercise 3   Draw Objects to Show How Many

Also available in print

 30 min **Problem-Based Interactive Learning**

Overview Children will learn to solve problems by using counters to act out the problem.

Focus How do you use counters to solve a problem?

Materials Counters (or Teaching Tool 32)

Set the Purpose *You have learned about ordering numbers. Today you will learn about how to use counters to solve a word problem.*

Connect Hold up 3 pencils. Ask children to show one finger for each pencil. *How many fingers?* Have a volunteer count the three fingers, one at a time. *How many pencils?* [3]

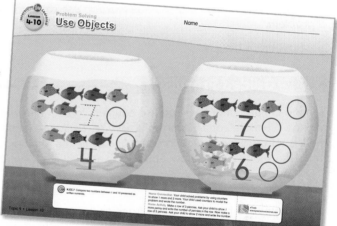
Sample answers shown.

MATHEMATICAL
PRACTICES

Use Appropriate Tools
Remind children they have learned how to order numbers 0–10.

Pose the Problem *First I see 6 fish in a bowl. Then I see 1 more fish. How many fish do I see now? How can I solve this problem?* Have children share their ideas.

Model Draw a fish bowl on the board with 6 fish in a row. *We can use counters to find out how many fish.* Draw a circle over one fish and say "one." Ask: *How can we count the rest of the fish?* Call on volunteers to each put a mark over one fish and say the next number until they reach 6. As each fish is marked off on the board, have children put one counter over a fish in the bowl on the workmat. Count the counters together. *I see 6 fish in a bowl and then I see 1 more fish. How many fish do I see?* Have children put another counter on the workmat, count on, and write the number 7. Continue with this problem: *I see 3 fish in a bowl and then I see 1 more fish. How many fish do I see?* [4] Have children trace counters.

Use Math Manipulatives Make sure children place one counter over each fish.

Small-Group Interaction Have partners complete the page as you pose these problems: *Kayla sees 5 fish and then 2 more. How many fish does she see?* [7] *Zack sees 4 fish and then 2 more. How many fish does he see?* [6]

Have partners circle the larger number and the bigger group of fish in each fish bowl. *How do you know which number is larger?*

eTools **Counters**
www.pearsonsuccessnet.com

Visual Learning

Read and Understand

How many frogs do you see? [3] *How many would there be with one more frog? How could we find out?* Have volunteers share their ideas.

Plan

Jake uses counters to count the frogs. How can we use Jake's counters to find out how many frogs? [We can count the counters.]

1 Visual Learning

Set the Purpose Point out the **Visual Learning Bridge** at the top of the page. *In this lesson, you will learn to use counters to solve a problem.*

2 Guided Practice

Remind children that they can use counters to count how many and to show "1 more" and "2 more." Exercise 1 allows children to revisit the **Visual Learning Bridge** to count and write the number for 1 more frog. The suggestions below apply to Exercises 1–8.

Error Intervention

If children have trouble keeping track as they count their tracings,

then have them mark an X on each tracing as they count it.

Do you understand? *How many counters do you put down for "1 more" frog?* [1] *How many counters do you put down for "2 more" birds?* [2]

Reteaching On chart paper, draw 5 balloons. Call on a volunteer to come up and circle one balloon, while children put one counter on a mat or table for the balloon. Continue this procedure with all 5 balloons. Help children to count the counters. Then draw 1 more balloon on the chart paper. *How can we find out how many balloons there are now?* Invite a volunteer to circle the balloon, while children add a counter to their workmat. *What number shows how many balloons there are now?* [6] Have children recount the counters to check.

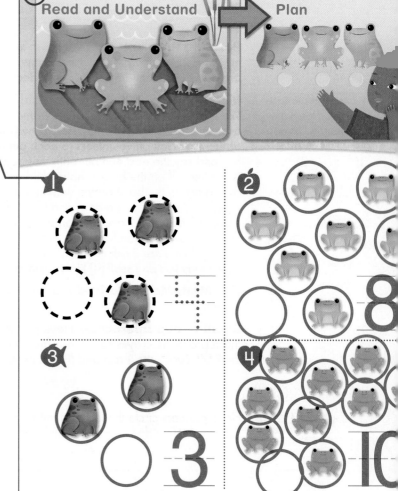

Directions Hillary sees frogs at the pond. Then she sees 1 more frog. How many frogs are there now? How can we ___ out? How can we use counters? Have children place a counter on each picture of a frog and show 1 more counter. ___ them to trace the counters and write the number.

Topic 4 • Lesson 10

Solve

What does Jake do to show one more frog? [He adds one more counter.]

Look Back and Check

4

What number should Jake write to show how many frogs in all? [4]

Solve

Look Back and Check

4

 6

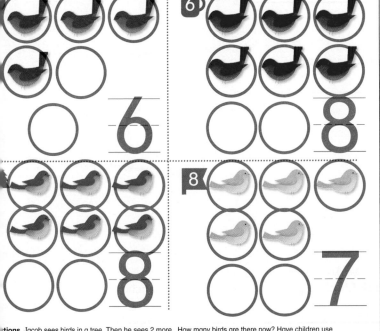

6

8

8

8

7

tions Jacob sees birds in a tree. Then he sees 2 more. How many birds are there now? Have children use ...ers and explain their answers. Then have them trace the counters and write the number.

Additional Activity

How Many More?

🕐 10–15 min 👫

Materials (per pair) 10 color tiles (or Teaching Tool 31)

- Partner A selects from 1 to 8 color tiles and lays them on the table. Both children count them aloud together.
- Partner B closes his or her eyes while Partner A adds either 1 or 2 more tiles to the group.
- Partner B opens his or her eyes and tells whether 1 more tile or 2 more tiles have been added to the original group.
- Partners switch roles and repeat.

---

3 **Independent Practice** Ⓒ MATHEMATICAL PRACTICES

Ⓒ **Use Appropriate Tools** Children use counters to show 2 more birds in each exercise. They trace the counters and write the numbers.

86A

Close

Essential Understanding Some problems can be solved by using objects to act out the actions in the problems. *You can use one counter for each object in a group. You can count the counters to find out how many. You can also use counters to help you add "1 more."*

 ASSESSMENT

Exercise 1 is worth 1 point.
Use the rubric to score Exercise 2.

Exercise 2

Use Appropriate Tools Children should be able to add 2 more counters to make, and then to write, the number 9.

E L L Model Thinking Aloud Demonstrate how to place a counter on each picture of an ant and then add 2 more counters. Touch each counter and count aloud.

Student Samples
3-point answer Children draw 9 counters and write 9.

2-point answer Children write the number but do not draw counters.

1-point answer Children draw an incorrect number of counters.

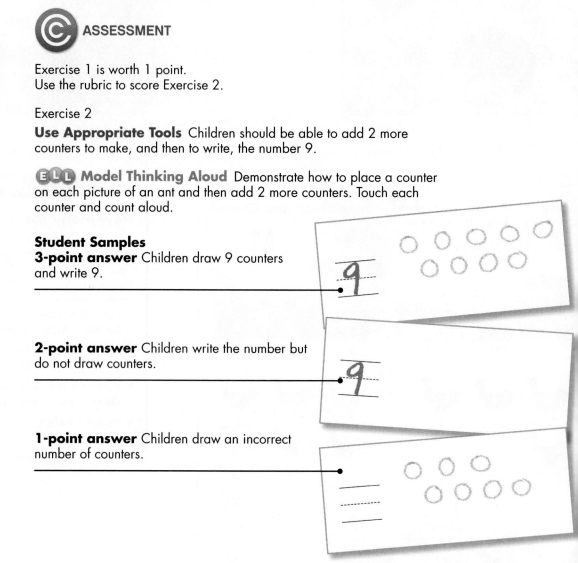

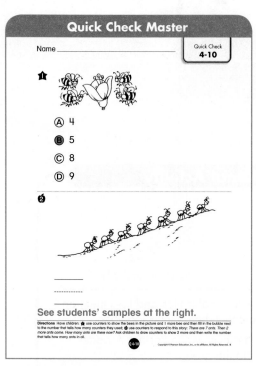

1.

Ⓐ 4
Ⓑ 5
Ⓒ 8
Ⓓ 9

2.

See students' samples at the right.

Directions Have children: ★ use counters to show the bees in the picture and 1 more bee and then fill in the bubble next to the number that tells how many counters they used; ❷ use counters to respond to this story: There are 7 ants. Then 2 more ants come. How many ants are there now? Ask children to draw counters to show 2 more and then write the number that tells how many ants in all.

4-10   Copyright © Pearson Education, Inc., or its affiliates. All Rights Reserved. K

Formative Assessment

Use the **Quick Check** to assess children's understanding.

Prescription for Differentiated Instruction
Use children's work on the **Quick Check** to prescribe differentiated instruction.

Points	Prescription
0–2	Intervention
3	On-Level
4	Advanced

Differentiated Instruction

Intervention

Use Ribbon

 15–20 min

Materials (per pair) 8 index cards with a picture of a ribbon or yarn on each one, 8 pieces of ribbon or yarn, a mat or sheet of paper

- Place 7 cards facedown in a row on a table above a workmat.

- Have a child turn over 1 index card and place 1 piece of ribbon on the mat. Continue this procedure until all the ribbon cards are turned over.

- Have children count the pieces of ribbon on the mat. Ask: *How many ribbons are there?*

- Then place another ribbon card next to the turned over cards. Ask: *How can we show "one more" ribbon?*

Practice **On-Level** **Center Activity**

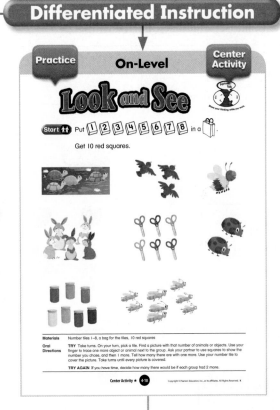

Practice **Advanced** **Center Activity**

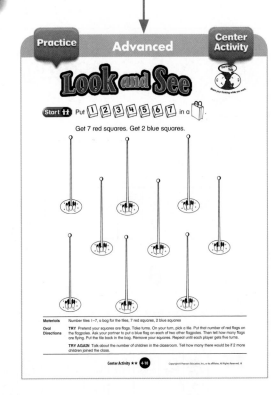

E L L Partner Talk Listen for the phrases *one more* or *two more*. For example, a child might say, "There are four turtles. If two more came we would see six turtles."

Leveled Homework

Reteaching Master

Practice Master

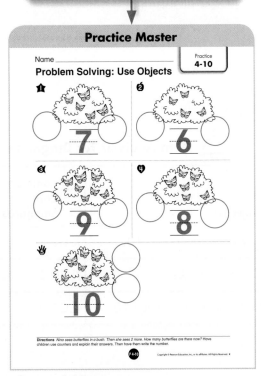

Enrichment Master

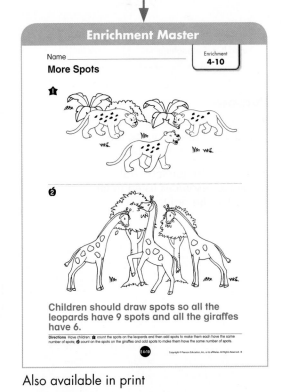

Also available in print

Also available in print

Also available in print

eTools **Counters**
www.pearsonsuccessnet.com

eTools **Geometry Shapes**
www.pearsonsuccessnet.com

eTools **Geometry Shapes**
www.pearsonsuccessnet.com

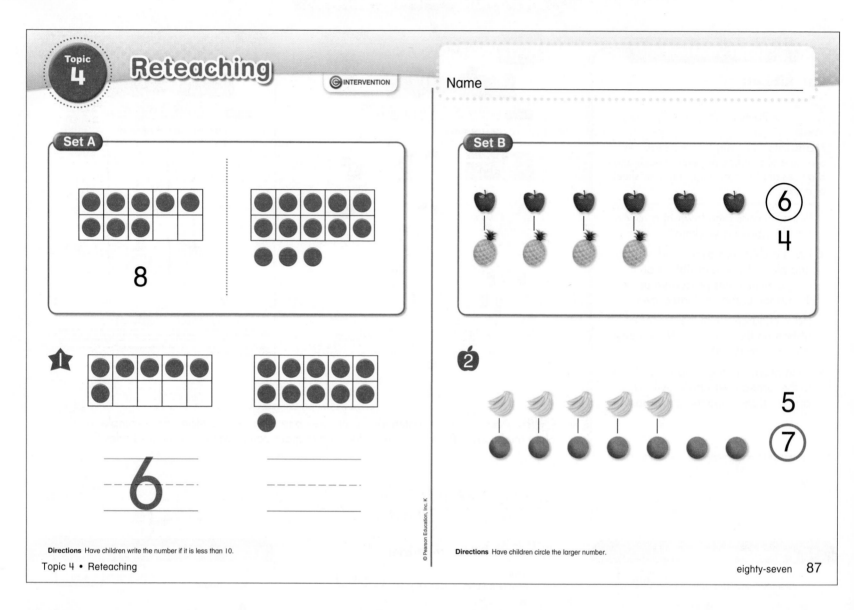

Reteaching · INTERVENTION

Name _____

Set A

8

★

6

Directions Have children write the number if it is less than 10.

Topic 4 · Reteaching

Set B

⑥
4

❷

5
⑦

© Pearson Education, Inc. K

Directions Have children circle the larger number.

eighty-seven 87

Purpose
- Provide children with more examples and practice for each lesson in the topic.
- For intervention materials, use the resources listed in the chart to the right.

Item Analysis for Diagnosis and Intervention

Objective	© Common Core Standards	Reteaching Sets	Student Book Lessons	Intervention System
Compare numbers to 10.	K.CC.6	Set A, 1	4-3	A11
Compare numbers.	K.CC.6	Set B, 2	4-1, 4-2	A4
Order numbers through 10.	K.CC.2	Set C, 3	4-8, 4-9	A11

INTERVENTION

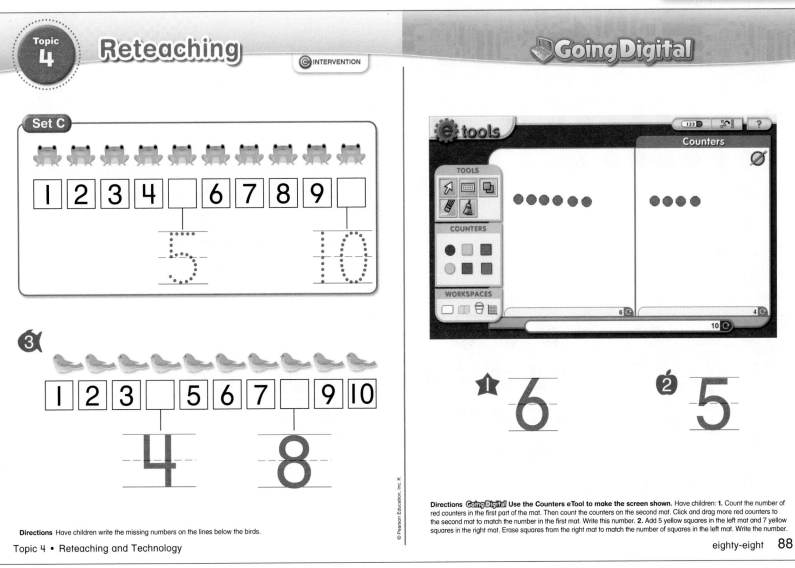

Topic 4 · Reteaching and Technology

Directions Have children write the missing numbers on the lines below the birds.

Directions **Going Digital** Use the Counters eTool to make the screen shown. Have children: **1.** Count the number of red counters in the first part of the mat. Then count the counters on the second mat. Click and drag more red counters to the second mat to match the number in the first mat. Write this number. **2.** Add 5 yellow squares in the left mat and 7 yellow squares in the right mat. Erase squares from the right mat to match the number of squares in the left mat. Write the number.

Response to Intervention

Ongoing Intervention
- Lessons with guiding questions to assess understanding
- Support to prevent misconceptions and to reteach

Strategic Intervention
- Targeted to small groups who need more support
- Easy to implement

Intensive Intervention
- Instruction to accelerate progress
- Instruction focused on foundational skills

Going Digital

Purpose
- Provide children with an opportunity to understand how to compare groups of objects by taking away from one group and adding to another.

Count the dots in each group. Which group has more? Drag a dot from the side to the one that has fewer. Challenge children to determine how many dots they need to drag over to the group before they begin.

Topic 4 Test

@ASSESSMENT

Name _____

1. (●●●●●●●●) 8
(●●●●●●) 6

Ⓐ 4
Ⓑ 6
Ⓒ 8
Ⓓ 10

4.

9
7

2.
Ⓐ
Ⓑ
Ⓒ
Ⓓ

3. 3
Ⓐ 4
Ⓑ 3
Ⓒ 2
Ⓓ 1

5.

| 6 | 4 |
| 3 | 5 |

3 4 5 6

Multiple-Choice Directions Have children mark the best answer. **1.** Which of these two numbers is greater? **2.** Which group of counters shows a number that is more than 5 and less than 10? **3.** Which group is 2 fewer than 3?

Constructed-Response Directions Have children: **4.** draw a line from each anthill to an ant, circle the group with more, write the numbers, and circle the number that is greater; **5.** write the numbers in the correct order.

Topic 4 • Test

eighty-nine **89**

Purpose
- Assess children's understanding of the concepts and skills in Topic 4 using multiple-choice and constructed response formats.
- Additional assessment options can be found in the Teacher Resource Masters.
- For intervention materials that correspond to all tests, use the resources listed in the chart to the right.

Test-Taking Tips

Discuss with children the following tips for test success.

Understand the Question
- Look for important words.
- Turn the question into a statement: "I need to find out…"

Gather Information
- Get information from text.
- Get information from pictures, maps, diagrams, tables, and graphs.

Make a Plan
- Think about problem-solving skills and strategies.
- Choose computation methods.

Make Smart Choices
- Eliminate wrong answers.
- Try working backward from an answer.
- Check answers for reasonableness; estimate.

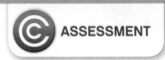
ASSESSMENT

 Item Analysis for Diagnosis and Intervention

Objective	ⓒ Common Core Standards	Test Items	Student Book Lessons	Intervention System
Find the greater number; find the number that is less.	K.CC.6	1, 2	4-1, 4-2, 4-3	A4, A11
Count to find 1 or 2 more or fewer.	K.CC.6	3	4-4, 4-5, 4-6, 4-7	A4
Solve problems using objects.	K.CC.7	4	4-10	A4, E13
Order numbers through 10.	K.CC.2	5	4-8, 4-9	

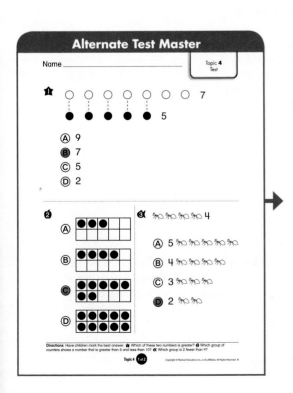

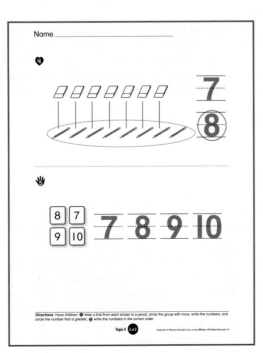

Topic 4 Performance Task ASSESSMENT

1

8

2

6

Directions Have children choose a number more than 5 and less than 10 and write that number above the first ten-frame. Have children draw counters in the ten-frame to show the number.

Topic 4 • Performance Task

Directions Have children draw 2 fewer counters in this ten-frame than the first ten-frame and then write that number above the ten-frame. Have children draw counters in the ten-frame to show the number.

ninety   90

Sample answers shown represent a possible 3-point answer.

Purpose Assess children's understanding of the concepts and skills in Topic 4 through a performance-based task.

Unifying Concept
Comparison and Relationships Numbers, expressions, measures, and objects can be compared and related to other numbers, expressions, measures, and objects in different ways.

Topic Essential Question How can numbers from 0 to 10 be compared and ordered?

Task For this assessment, children draw counters.

Get Ready Review with children how to compare groups of objects to find which has more or fewer objects.

Guiding the Activity Explain to children that there are 2 ten-frames on the page. Remind them to draw counters in each frame and then write the number for each frame on the lines.

Questioning Strategies Did you choose a number more than 5 and less than 10 for the first frame? How many counters did you draw in the first ten-frame? Did you draw 2 fewer counters in the second ten-frame? How do you know?

Scoring Rubric

3-point answer The child chooses and writes a number that is more than 5 and less than 10, and draws the correct number of counters in the first frame. Then the child draws 2 fewer counters in the second frame and writes the number.

2-point answer The child chooses and writes a number that is more than 5 and less than 10, and draws the correct number of counters in the first frame. Then the child draws 2 fewer counters in the second frame but may have difficulty writing the number that is 2 fewer than the chosen number.

1-point answer The child makes an attempt, but needs assistance to complete the steps of the activity.

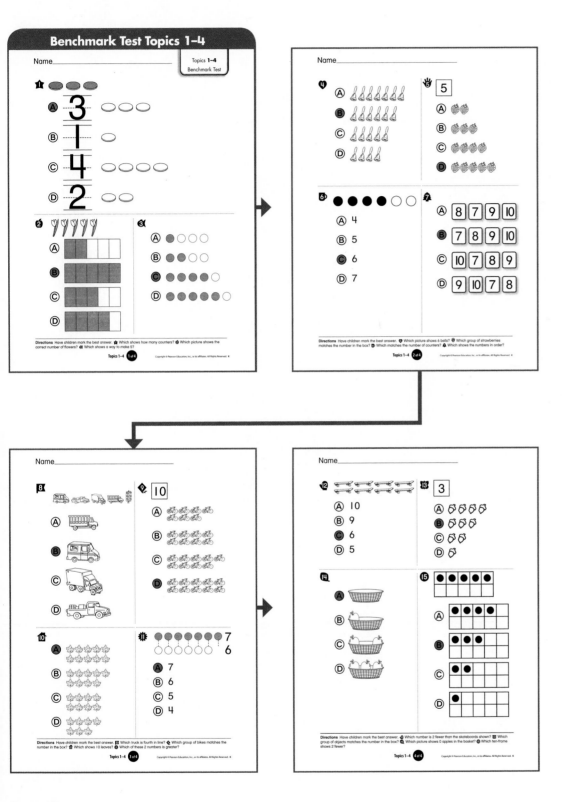

Purpose

• Assess content that is taught in Topics 1–4.